FOLENS IDEAS BA

RE: SPECIAL PEOPLE

Louis Fidge
John Williams

Contents

How to use this book

Ideas Bank books provide you with ready to use, practical photocopiable activity pages for your pupils **plus** a wealth of ideas for extension and development.

TEACHER IDEAS PAGE | **PHOTOCOPIABLE ACTIVITY PAGE**

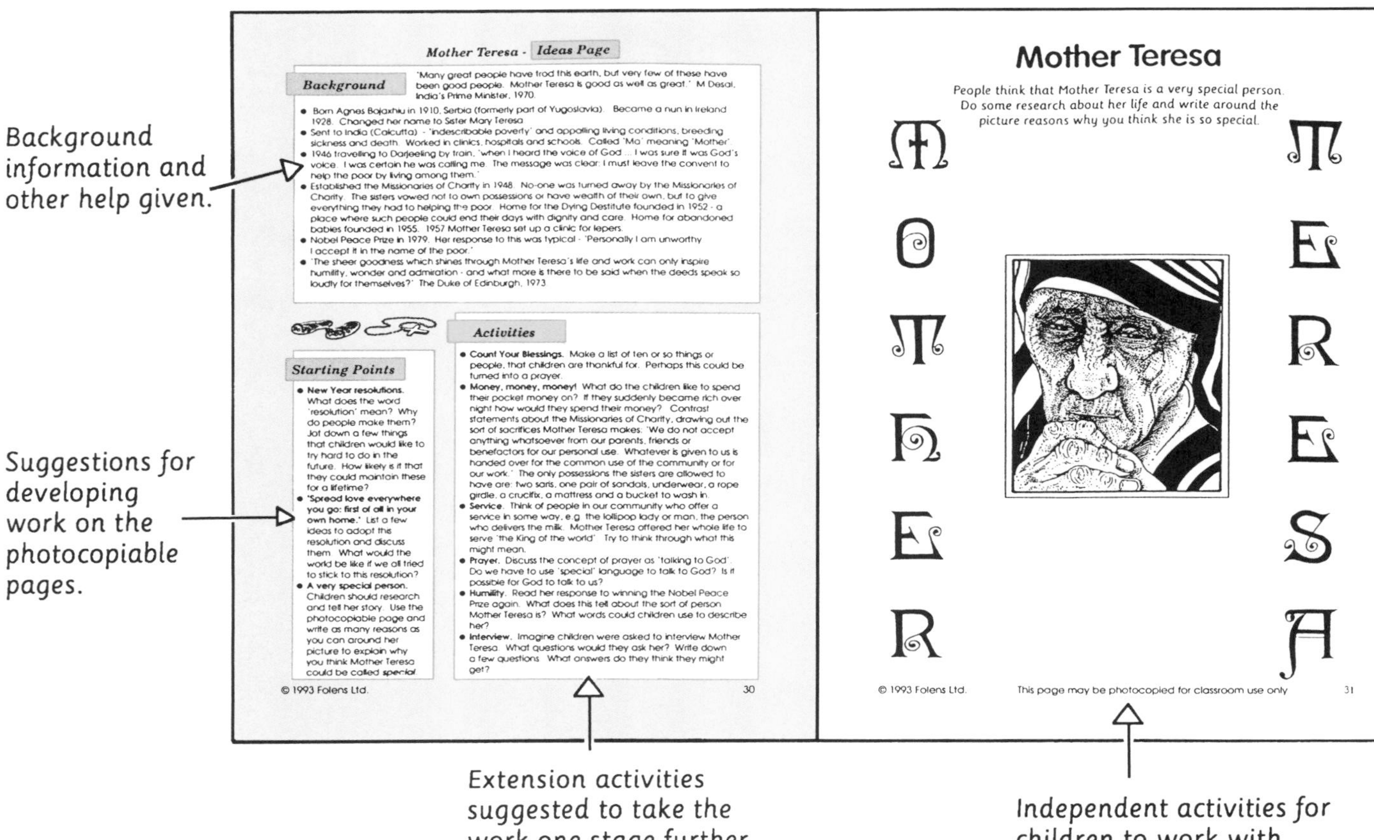

Mother Teresa - Ideas Page

Background

'Many great people have trod this earth, but very few of these have been good people. Mother Teresa is good as well as great.' M Desai, India's Prime Minister, 1970.

- Born Agnes Bojaxhiu in 1910, Serbia (formerly part of Yugoslavia). Became a nun in Ireland 1928. Changed her name to Sister Mary Teresa.
- Sent to India (Calcutta) - 'indescribable poverty' and appalling living conditions, breeding sickness and death. Worked in clinics, hospitals and schools. Called 'Ma' meaning 'Mother'.
- 1946 travelling to Darjeeling by train, 'when I heard the voice of God ... I was sure it was God's voice. I was certain he was calling me. The message was clear: I must leave the convent to help the poor by living among them.'
- Established the Missionaries of Charity in 1948. No-one was turned away by the Missionaries of Charity. The sisters vowed not to own possessions or have wealth of their own, but to give everything they had to helping the poor. Home for the Dying Destitute founded in 1952 - a place where such people could end their days with dignity and care. Home for abandoned babies founded in 1955. 1957 Mother Teresa set up a clinic for lepers.
- Nobel Peace Prize in 1979. Her response to this was typical - 'Personally I am unworthy I accept it in the name of the poor.'
- 'The sheer goodness which shines through Mother Teresa's life and work can only inspire humility, wonder and admiration - and what more is there to be said when the deeds speak so loudly for themselves?' The Duke of Edinburgh, 1973

Starting Points

- **New Year resolutions.** What does the word 'resolution' mean? Why do people make them? Jot down a few things that children would like to try hard to do in the future. How likely is it that they could maintain these for a lifetime?
- **'Spread love everywhere you go: first of all in your own home.'** List a few ideas to adopt this resolution and discuss them. What would the world be like if we all tried to stick to this resolution?
- **A very special person.** Children should research and tell her story. Use the photocopiable page and write as many reasons as you can around her picture to explain why you think Mother Teresa could be called special.

Activities

- **Count Your Blessings.** Make a list of ten or so things or people, that children are thankful for. Perhaps this could be turned into a prayer.
- **Money, money, money!** What do the children like to spend their pocket money on? If they suddenly became rich over night how would they spend their money? Contrast statements about the Missionaries of Charity, drawing out the sort of sacrifices Mother Teresa makes: 'We do not accept anything whatsoever from our parents, friends or benefactors for our personal use. Whatever is given to us is handed over for the common use of the community or for our work.' The only possessions the sisters are allowed to have are: two saris, one pair of sandals, underwear, a rope girdle, a crucifix, a mattress and a bucket to wash in.
- **Service.** Think of people in our community who offer a service in some way, e.g. the lollipop lady or man, the person who delivers the milk. Mother Teresa offered her whole life to serve 'the King of the world'. Try to think through what this might mean.
- **Prayer.** Discuss the concept of prayer as 'talking to God'. Do we have to use 'special' language to talk to God? Is it possible for God to talk to us?
- **Humility.** Read her response to winning the Nobel Peace Prize again. What does this tell about the sort of person Mother Teresa is? What words could children use to describe her?
- **Interview.** Imagine children were asked to interview Mother Teresa. What questions would they ask her? Write down a few questions. What answers do they think they might get?

© 1993 Folens Ltd. 30

Mother Teresa

People think that Mother Teresa is a very special person. Do some research about her life and write around the picture reasons why you think she is so special.

MOTHER TERESA

© 1993 Folens Ltd. This page may be photocopied for classroom use only 31

- Time saving, relevant and practical, **Ideas Bank** books ensure that you will always have work ready at hand.

Folens books are protected by international copyright laws. All rights reserved. The copyright of all materials in this book, except where otherwise stated, remains the property of the publisher and author(s). No part of this publication may be reproduced, stored in a retrieval system, or transmitted, in any form or by any means, for whatever purpose, without the written permission of Folens Limited.

Folens do allow photocopying of selected pages of this publication for educational use, providing that this use is within the confines of the purchasing institution. You may make as many copies as you require for classroom use of the pages so marked.

This resource may be used in a variety of ways; however it is not intended that teachers or students should write into the book itself.

© 1993 Folens Limited, on behalf of the author.

Cover by: In Touch Creative Services Ltd. Illustrations by: Dandi Palmer. Cover photograph © P. Emmett.

First published 1993 by Folens Limited, Albert House, Apex Business Centre, Boscombe Road, Dunstable, LU5 4RL, England.
Reprinted 1999.

ISBN 185276519-4

Introduction

A frequent claim made by educators is that the purpose of education is to educate the whole child, catering for the child's spiritual, moral, social, emotional, aesthetic and intellectual development. The reality in many primary schools, however, is somewhat different. Children's spiritual development is frequently given a low priority, according to the **REACH** research.

It is easy to understand why this might be. The advent of the National Curriculum has placed enormous burdens on the already hard-pressed teacher. On top of this, RE is a subject about which many feel uncertain, anxious or insecure. The **REACH** research suggests that many feel they have insufficient personal knowledge, especially if they don't espouse any particular faith themselves. Another concern is that too little training is given and that there is a lack of good resources which are easily accessible and usable in the primary classroom. ***Special People*** is designed to help address this latter concern.

Over the last few years there have been many serious attempts to 'map out' more systematically what it is believed RE teaching in schools should involve. By looking at two different attempts to analyse the issues it is possible to see common ground between them. The view is emerging that RE teaching should include:

a) **a 'knowledge' component** relating to important facts, information and concepts

b) **an 'experience' component** helping children reflect on, and respond to, their experiences so that knowledge can lead to understanding and insight.

The 'knowledge' component

The **FARE** Project identified three important areas:

- *Religious Belief and Commitment* (and how they are applied to everyday life and demonstrated through sacred writings and key religious figures)
- *Religious Practice* (focusing on things like worship, prayer, celebration, pilgrimage, etc.)
- *Religious Language* (looking at different means of experience, e.g. through religious symbolism and key religious concepts like sacrifice).

Bedfordshire's RE Guidelines explore knowledge about religion through themes such as:

Writings *People* *Worship* *Places*
Festivals and Celebrations *Rites and Rules.*

The 'experience' component

The **FARE** Project suggests three areas of importance. These are:

Reflection on Meaning - This involves encouraging children to reflect on themselves, their inner feelings and their relationships with others. It involves raising children's awareness of a sense of mystery, awe and wonder.

Questions of Meaning - This involves helping pupils to explore questions of meaning and purpose, encouraging their own personal search for meaning.

Values and Commitments - This involves understanding how these influence attitudes and behaviour, understanding the possibility of making a personal commitment, and developing a sensitivity to the beliefs and commitments of others.

Bedfordshire's RE Guidelines talk about the 'Reflection and Response to Human Experience' and consider two themes:

Self and Others - helping pupils to develop an understanding of themselves and other people, their relationships to each other and human relationships.

Natural World - helping pupils to explore and reflect on the world around them.

Special People resources provide accessible, flexible and immediate support for RE teaching. The units include background information on each topic, as well as ample opportunities for extending and developing them further if appropriate. Each unit may be treated as a single lesson, although potentiallly each could be extended to cover up to a half-term's work.

The resources include a wide range of stimulating and relevant activities capable of being used across a wide age and ability range. The teaching notes include starting points for introducing main ideas and further activities for extension and follow-up. Each unit is accompanied by a photocopiable activity. These vary in style and purpose. For example, sometimes the activity could be in the form of a game introducing the main idea; sometimes it is something like a sequencing activity to be used during the main body of the lesson; sometimes the sheet might be used as a concluding activity.

Special People resources may be used as a coherent programme of RE activities. They have been divided into sections and logically sequenced to allow for this if required. Alternatively the units may be used selectively in any order according to need. Each unit has been designed to be free-standing. The resources may also be used as part of topic or thematic work in a more cross-curricular context. The materials also make ideal topics for assemblies/collective worship.

Practical teaching suggestions are made throughout. There is no set pattern for using or teaching each unit. However, by and large it is expected that there will be a class teaching element when the topic is introduced, along with opportunities for small group, paired and individual activities.

Much emphasis is placed on the importance of first-hand experience, and in using and sharing children's existing knowledge. Frequent opportunities are created for discussion and reflection on different points of view. The materials provide a range of thought-provoking activities to stimulate discussion and questions. Role play, drama and games are also used for this purpose.

An essential part of the learning process in RE is to allow children to come to terms with their own experiences and thoughts, to be encouraged to articulate them as part of their own individual search for meaning. The teacher's role here is to create the opportunity for this to happen. The ideal context is a supportive classroom atmosphere of trust to encourage pupils to do just this.

Children's responses to the material will often be through discussion, but there are also many occasions when they are asked to record their thoughts in writing or in visual form.

Assessment of the knowledge component of RE is relatively easy as it is possible to be more objective. The development of the individual's spiritual understanding is more subjective and therefore difficult to assess, but the variety of spoken and written activities provide plenty of opportunities for gaining insights into this area of development.

References

REACH Religious Education and Collective Worship in Primary Schools, Culham College Institute, Abingdon, 1992

The FARE Project, Interim Report, Exeter University, School of Education, 1990

Bedfordshire's Attainment and Assessment in RE Draft Guidelines 1991

Myself, Family and Friends - Ideas Page

Aim

The aim of this theme is to raise awareness of what it means to be 'special' within a known and personal context and to identify human qualities associated with being 'special'.

Starting Points

- **Focus on the individual.** Every individual is unique. Begin by considering physical differences - age, sex, height, appearance, etc. Discuss uniqueness of fingerprints. Make 'thumb-print' pictures. Ask the class to bring in 'baby' pictures and discuss how they have changed. Move on to thinking about other sorts of things that make individuals different.
- We all have our own personalities, attitudes, likes and dislikes. Ask children to write down anonymously ten things about themselves. Read them aloud. Play a 'Guess Who' game.
- **Everyone is special and unique to God.** Psalm 139, v13-14 says 'For you (God) created my inmost being; you knit me together in my mother's womb. I praise you because I am fearfully and wonderfully made.' Discuss what this could mean.

Activities

- **Special People I know.** Share with the class, in a personal, anecdotal way, memories or thoughts about a number of people (family, relatives and friends) who are special to you and explain why. *I will always remember my Uncle Bert. He always seemed to have time to sit and talk ...* Ask children to talk about some people who are 'special' to them.
- Use the photocopiable sheet and ask the class to draw five people (family, friends, relatives) who are 'special' in some way. Within a small group take it in turns to discuss with each other who the people are and explain why they have been chosen. Do they all live nearby? How often do you see them? Are they all alive?

- **What makes someone special?** What sorts of things were said about - parents? grandparents? friends? Try to draw out common underlying qualities and characteristics of people, e.g. prepared to listen, cares for me, generous, thoughtful, forgives me when I am naughty, etc. Write single words or phrases on board/ OHP as they are mentioned. Ask children to explain what they think each phrase means. Ask for examples of the sorts of things a person with these characteristics or qualities might do. To finish, ask children to write underneath each picture they have drawn, the sorts of qualities or characteristics these people have.
- **A Perfect Friend.** If children could make up a very special friend of their own, a perfect friend, a friend with no faults, what qualities would he/she have?
- **List poems.** Focus on things people do to make them special:

  My Mum cooks for me
  My Mum tucks me in bed at night
  My Mum ...

  A friend is someone who calls for you to play
  A friend is someone who lets you join in their games
  A friend is someone who ...

- **Acrostics.** Write a poem about someone special. The first letter of each line spells his/her name.
- **Special People in the Past.** Ask parents or grandparents to think back and talk about people who were special to them when they were children. Can they find any photos of them? Is there anyone in a family history who has done anything really different or special? Trace back some relatives and draw a simple family tree.
- **Maths.** Use the pictures drawn by children for data collection. How can you sort the pictures into categories? Which categories of people appeared most? least? Discuss why this might have happened. Represent this graphically.
- **Collage.** Use the pictures drawn by children to make a class collage of 'Our Very Special People'.

© 1993 Folens Ltd.

Myself, Family and Friends

Use these frames to draw or paste pictures of special people you know.

- *Write their names in the frames.*
- *Talk about why these people are special.*

© 1993 Folens Ltd. This page may be photocopied for classroom use only

Special People In My Community - Ideas Page

Aim

The aim of this theme is to raise awareness of what it means to be 'special' within the known and personal context of the local community and to identify qualities associated with being 'special'.

Starting Points

- What is a community? Discuss with the class what they understand by 'local community'. Try to identify what characterises a 'community'.
- **Who is special?** Working in pairs, ask children to think of people (not family or friends) in the immediate locality who they consider 'special' in some way. (Don't try to explain the term 'special' to them at this stage.) Each pair should come up with a single written list between them. Next, get each pair to cut up their list of names so that each one is separate. Between them, select who they think the six most 'special' people are from their list. Discuss and negotiate choices. Justify inclusion in or exclusion from the top six. Ask children to draw and name pictures of their chosen six people.
- **Classify people according to role.** On the board/OHP try sorting the names of the people children chose into groups according to the job or role the people have, e.g. shopkeepers, people who keep us safe, people in authority, people who visit the school regularly, spiritual leaders, etc. Consider what makes these people special.
- **Characteristics or categories of people.** Draw out common underlying qualities and characteristics specific groups of people have: e.g. they serve us; they are helpful/caring; they make sure I am kept safe; they are powerful/important; they have authority; they have a special skill, etc. Write single words or phrases on the board/OHP as they are mentioned.
- Ask children to use these ideas and get them to write underneath each picture they have drawn the sorts of qualities or characteristics these people have, e.g.
  Mrs _____ is special because she ____________ .

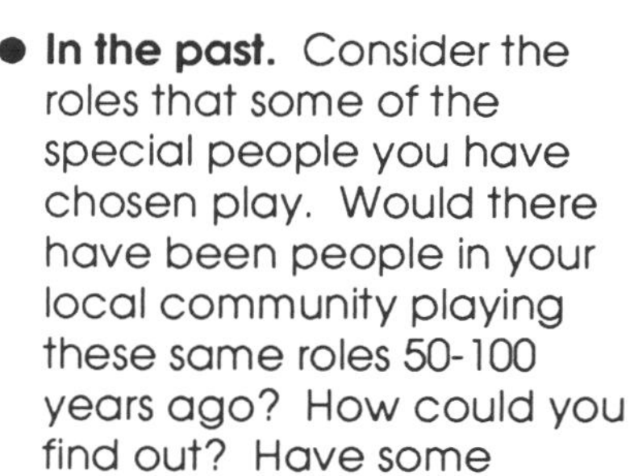

Activities

- **Characteristics of special people in the community.** Use the resource sheet grid as a way of categorising various people in the community identified as 'special'. Discuss the headings first to ensure words like 'authority' are understood. Note that some people may be ticked in more than one column.
- **Guess Who.** Ask children to think of some adult in the school and write three or four sentences about the person without actually mentioning their name. Can others guess who is being described?
- **Role Playing.** Act out situations featuring some of the special people mentioned. Imagine how they would respond and the sorts of things they might say.
- **The Special Visitor.** Ask the children to imagine that they had a very special visitor at school. (Think about who it might be.) Would they behave differently from normal? How? Why? If they were asked to show the visitor around what sort of things would they point out and talk about? What sort of things would they miss out and not talk about?
- **In the past.** Consider the roles that some of the special people you have chosen play. Would there have been people in your local community playing these same roles 50-100 years ago? How could you find out? Have some 'special' jobs disappeared? Have some new ones been created? Why?
- **Using a local map.** On a large map of your local community locate where your special people live or work.
- **Music.** Is it possible to link in any relevant music about the sorts of people mentioned? Victorian street traders' songs, etc.

Special People In My Community

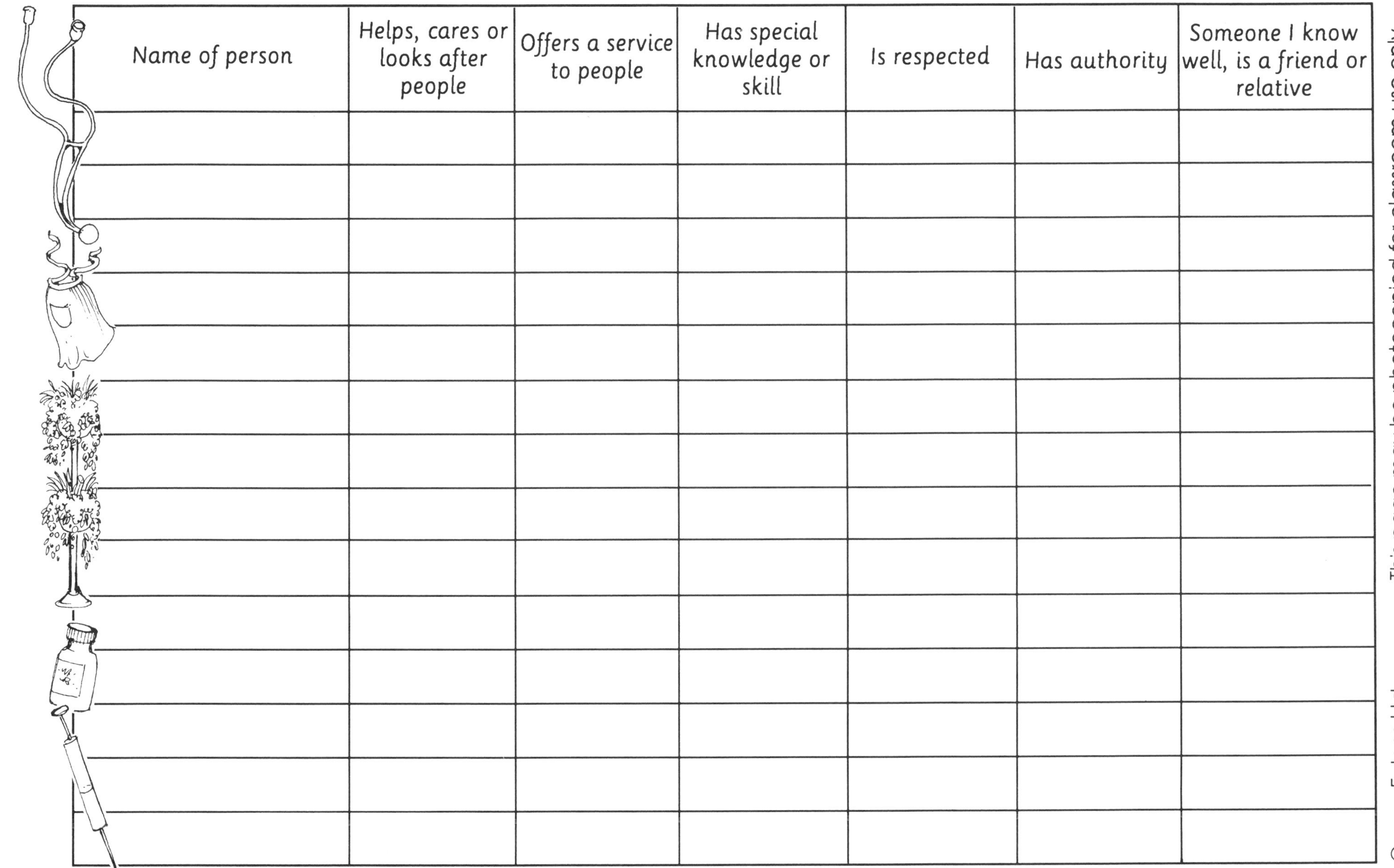

Name of person	Helps, cares or looks after people	Offers a service to people	Has special knowledge or skill	Is respected	Has authority	Someone I know well, is a friend or relative

© Folens Ltd. This page may be photocopied for classroom use only

Guess Who - Ideas Page

Aim

The aim of this theme is to think about people who are well-known and to consider in what ways they might be thought of as 'special'.

Starting Points

- **Guess who!** Get the children to cut out and piece together the jigsaw puzzle showing Henry VIII. Explain that it is a picture of a well-known person from our past. (Sticking the whole sheet to thin card first will make the task easier.) When the puzzle is complete ask how many children recognise the character. What is known about him? Why is he famous?
- **The Famous Five.** Ask the children to write down the names of five famous living people they admire whom they consider special in some way. The people could be from entertainment, sport, politics, etc. Ask them to discuss their choices with a partner, explaining exactly why they like the particular people and what they think is special about them. Discuss this as a whole class. Are there any names that have been mentioned several times? Who? Why is this?
- **Discussion.** Select one of the named people and discuss why they are popular. Are they popular with all of the class or only with a certain group, e.g. boys or girls? Would the same people be equally popular with other age groups? Would they be as popular with parents or grandparents? Ask children to get their parents to undertake the same activity and to compare the results with the children's. Would they be as popular with people in other cultures? Are all famous people special?
  - How have different people become well-known?
  - Why are we so interested in special people?
  - How do they influence us (our thinking, attitudes, lifestyle, appearance, aspirations, etc.)?
  - Do all people we consider 'special' influence us for the good?

Activities

- **Categorising what makes people special.** Write out a selection of the names the children offered in the 'Famous Five' activity. Try to categorise the people. Are the people special because:
  - they have a definite skill or talent that is valued?
  - they entertain us?
  - they have a dynamic personality or because of their physical appearance?
  - they have special knowledge of some sort?
  - of their important position in society?
  - they are frequently in the public eye?
- **Developing the theme.** Collect together the names. Is there a common thread? Which areas of life do the people come from? Is it possible to develop headings such as Entertainment, Sport, Politics, The Royal Family, Religion, etc? Write each heading on a separate large sheet of paper and divide the sheets into two columns. Enter the names in the left-hand column. Pin the sheets on the wall. Discuss the categories with the children. Ask them to find out and write on the names of other people in these categories. They could also try to bring in pictures of each. In the second column, opposite each name ask them to write a sentence giving one reason why that person is special.
- **Special people from the past.** Build up a gallery of important historical characters. Ask the children to try to think of as many special people from the past as possible. Research some of them. It would be possible to establish a sub-category of famous religious people from the past too.
- **Fictional Characters.** What fictional characters are special to the children? How many can they name and talk about?

© 1993 Folens Ltd.

Guess Who

Put together the pieces to find a special person. Talk about what is known about him and why he is famous.

© 1993 Folens Ltd. This page may be photocopied for classroom use only

Lost in the Jungle - Ideas Page

Aim

The aim of this theme is to think through aspects of leadership and to consider various leadership qualities.

Starting Points

- **A leader who is personally known.** Discuss a leader who is personally known to the children in the community, e.g. a teacher, the mayor. Think about the role the individual plays.
  - What are their responsibilities?
  - Is it an easy job? What does it entail?
  - Is it necessary to have such a person? Would it be possible to manage without them?
  - In what ways did they become leaders? Did they choose to become leaders?
  - How do they execute their role as a leader? What is their 'style' of leadership? Do they make rules? Are they consistent?
- **Discuss a public leader** (like the Prime Minister or member of the Royal Family).
- **Lost in the jungle.** Play the 'Lost in the Jungle' game in pairs as a lead-in to the main activity. Two counters and a coin are needed. Toss the coin to decide who starts first. Then use the coin as a die - toss the coin each turn, heads move 2 spaces, tails move 1 space.

Activities

- **Set the scene.** A plane has crashed in the middle of a remote jungle. The children are the only survivors. Discuss the problems and some possible situations they might have to deal with.
- **Discuss the importance of selecting a leader.** What would the problems be without one? What sort of qualities or skills would the leader need? Should the leader be male or female, or doesn't it matter? What would be the fairest way to choose one?
- **Deciding on a leader.** The group has to discuss among themselves, and to end up with a named person (or perhaps two). It is best to allocate a time limit for this (say 10-15 minutes).
- **Discussing the decision-making process.** Together, discuss what happened. Who was chosen? How? Why?
- **Briefing the leader/s.** Take the appointed leader/s to one side to brief them. Explain that:
  - they now have to prove themselves as leaders and have the responsibility for leading their group. They have to suggest a plan to get the group back to safety.

  Give the leader/s time to jot down their ideas. Report back to the group/s, make their proposals, and see how the group/s respond(s) and deal with their responses.
- **Briefing the group/s.** (NB The leader/s should not be party to the group briefing.) Each individual has to decide what they think of the suggestions. They have to consider how they want to respond. Should they support their leaders without question (even if they disagree with them)? Should they make their suggestions and comments known even if it means disagreeing? State that there are no right or wrong ways of carrying on the group discussions.
- **Leadership in action.** Allow the leader/s to put their proposals to the group/s and discuss them.
- **Review.** Report back and discuss the exercise, especially the outcomes. Draw out the important aspects of leadership.

Extensions

- **Writing or drama.** The 'Lost in the Jungle' game might well lead on to writing a story or some drama work about being lost in the jungle. Perhaps a tape recorder could be used for including sound and musical effects. A diary of events, like a captain's log, is another possibility.
- **Play a 'trust' game.** Work in pairs. One partner is blindfolded, the other person is responsible for guiding the partner around obstacles, using only verbal instructions.
- **Rules.** Make up a poster containing rules for having a civilised discussion in a group!
- **If I ruled the world ...** is a good theme for considering what changes might be made.

© 1993 Folens Ltd.

Lost in the Jungle

This page may be photocopied for classroom use only
© 1993 Folens Ltd.

Moses - Ideas Page

Background

- 2000 BC 'covenant' between God and Israelites - sets them aside as God's 'chosen people'.
- By 1300 BC Israelites slaves in Egypt. Moses born. Hidden in basket in bullrushes to avoid persecution and slavery by Egyptians. Found by Pharaoh's daughter. Brought up in Pharaoh's court as daughter's son. *(Exodus 2:1-10)*
- In anger Moses killed an Egyptian for beating a slave. Fled for his life. *(Exodus 2:11-25)*
- At Mount Horeb - experience of God in form of Burning Bush. Realised his mission was to rescue Jews from slavery and take them to the 'Promised Land'. *(Exodus 3:1-6)*
- Pharaoh refused to release Jews. Ten plagues sent to torment the Egyptians. Final plague (killing first-born Egyptian sons) persuaded Pharaoh. Moses led the Jews out of Egypt. *(Exodus 7-12)*
- Pharaoh pursued them with an army. God opened Red Sea for the Jews to cross in safety but the Egyptian army drowned. *(Exodus 14:10-29)*
- Moses took Jews to Mount Sinai, where he sought God's guidance for the future. *(Exodus 15-18)*
- God forgave the Jews for worshipping idols and renewed his covenant with them. *(Exodus 32:1-20)*
- Moses presented the Jews with Ten Commandments (a code for living by). *(Exodus 20:1-17, 34:1-9)*
- For forty years Moses led Jews through the wilderness to the 'Promised Land'. *(Numbers 10-27)*
- Selfless - on his death he told Joshua to lead Jews to 'Promised Land'. *(Numbers 27:12-23)*
- Jews regard Moses as the greatest of all prophets - they called him *Moshe Rabbenu* (our teacher-rabbi Moses). Pentateuch (first five books of the Bible) were attributed to Moses.

Starting Points

- **What is known already.** Set the context of the Jewish faith by using visuals, artefacts, visit to synagogue, etc. Explain the significance of the Old Testament to Jews.
- **Tell his story.** Use the pictures on the sheet to introduce the story of Moses. Looking at each picture one at a time, and using the background information, Bible references and other reference material, discuss the story.
- **Using the resource sheet.** Children work in pairs. Cut out one set of pictures between them. On a board /OHP list the key words:

  Bullrushes, Taskmaster, Burning Bush, Plagues, Red Sea, Mt Sinai, Idol worship, Ten Commandments, Wilderness wanderings, Joshua.

  Each pair has to match the correct word with each picture to sequence the story correctly.
- In groups of five, give each child two of the ten illustrations. The group must then decide the correct order and re-tell the story.
- Children could act out the key events, or compose their own cartoon-type pictures, as a way of reinforcing the story.

Activities

Use each picture to discuss:

- **Bullrushes.** The lengths Moses' parents went to, to protect him. What sacrifices are we prepared to make for friends/ family?
- **Taskmaster.** Slavery and social injustice. How can we deal with bullies?
- **Burning Bush.** Spiritual awareness of God. Do we ever take time to listen? Does God talk to us? How?
- **Plagues.** It took ten plagues before success came. Are we patient and determined or do we give up at the first hurdle? Each plague could be illustrated and the pictures sequenced.
- **Red Sea.** Demonstrates a faith and trust in God and his supernatural power.
- **Mount Sinai.** Who would we turn to when we need advice or guidance?
- **Idol worship.** When the Jews forgot God and worshipped idols, God was able to forgive them. Do we seek revenge? Is it easy to forgive?
- **Ten Commandments.** Make Ten Commandments for the school or community to live by.
- **Wilderness wanderings.** What sort of problems and frustrations might they have encountered? What qualities of leadership would Moses have had to display?
- **Joshua.** Moses reaches the 'Promised Land' - but does not take the Jews into it. He hands over the task to a younger man. What does 'being selfish' mean?

© 1993 Folens Ltd.

Moses

© 1993 Folens Ltd. This page may be photocopied for classroom use only

Background

- First of ten gurus (spiritual leaders) whom Sikhs revere. Sent to reveal God's word, although Sikhs also recognise Buddha, Moses, Jesus, Muhammad and Gandhi. (Sikh means 'to learn'.)
- Born in Muslim India 1469 into the 'warrior' class of society (allowed to study the Hindu scriptures).
- Reputedly could talk at birth. Displayed greater knowledge than Hindu priest at temple. Soon learned Sanskrit, Persian and Arabic.
- At 16 became an accountant. Spent spare time learning about Islam and Hinduism. Rejected both. Believed God was above human experience and not represented adequately by these religions.
- Regularly prayed by the Ganges river. One morning he did not return - thought drowned. Three days later he reappeared, transformed. He said he had been transported to 'God's court' and been commanded to teach people about God. The Sikh religion was born.
- Five key principles: the oneness of God (as represented by the ik onkar symbol) and the futility of religious divisions; the importance of serving and caring for others; the obligation of hospitality; the duty to defend the weak; the equality of all people, men and women, rich or poor, in the eyes of God, contrary to the prevalent caste system.
- One day entertained by a wealthy banker. Nanak gave him a needle to take into next life. Banker realised this was impossible, Nanak explained that it was also impossible to take all his money with him. We are only remembered for the good we do while on earth! Banker immediately gave all his money to the poor.
- Once caused great upset and offence to Muslims because his feet were pointing towards their holy building, the mosque, when asleep. Nanak replied that this was only a building, and that God resides in the hearts of individuals and not in any building.
- Nanak wrote poems in the form of songs. 974 of these have been preserved and form the basis of the Sikh scriptures - Guru Granth Sahib.
- Nanak settled with his family at Kartapur 1521. A gurdwara (Sikh place of worship) built. Died 1539.

Starting Points

- **What is known already?** Set in context by using artefacts, visits to Sikh temple, etc.
- **Tell his story.** Use the background information and the sequence of pictures to tell the life of Guru Nanak.
- **Using the resource sheet.** Ask the children to work in pairs. Cut out one set of the pictures between them. On a board/OHP list the key words:

  Born talking, Temple teacher, Accountant, Mysterious disappearance, Oneness of God, Serving and caring for others, You can't take it with you!, The mosque, Music and poetry, Kartapur.
- Each pair has to match the correct caption to the correct picture and sequence, re-telling the story of Guru Nanak.

Activities

Use each picture to discuss:

- **Born talking.** Could this have been a sign that Nanak was destined to be a special person? What signs told the world that Christ was going to be special too?
- **Temple.** Compare the temple scene with that of Jesus when he was twelve years old. *(Luke 2:39-52)*
- **Working as an accountant.** What sort of activities would this job have involved Nanak in? Compare and contrast the early career of Jesus before his ministry.
- **Mysterious disappearance.** Children imagine they were detectives and find Nanak's clothes by the riverside. What would they do? Compare the baptism of Jesus with the annointment of Guru Nanak. Why is water such a strong symbol in these stories?
- **Oneness of God.** Draw the ik onkar symbol with the opening words of the Sikh morning prayer:
  There is one God
  Eternal truth is his name.
- **Caring for others.** What examples of service and care can children cite in relation to home, school and the immediate environment?
- **Wealth.** Compare and contrast Nanak's story of the rich man with the parable of the rich man in *Luke 1*.
- **The mosque.** Draw and discuss features of gurdwaras (Sikh places of worship).
- **Music and poetry.** Is it easier to remember words when set to music? Much of Nanak's teaching is set to music in hymns. Explore different types of sacred music.
- **Kartapur.** Develop the importance of family life.

© 1993 Folens Ltd.

Guru Nanak

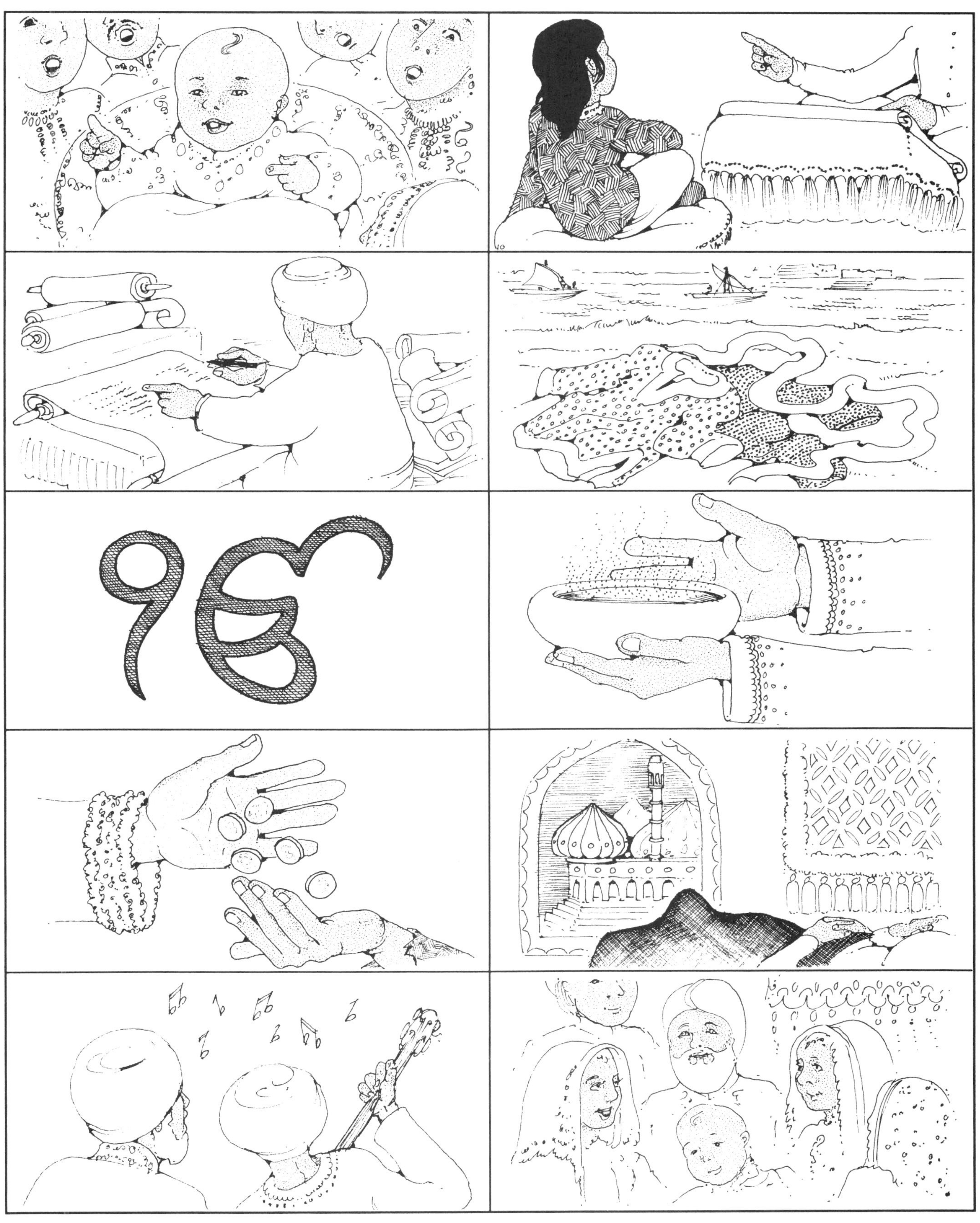

© 1993 Folens Ltd. This page may be photocopied for classroom use only

Muhammad - Ideas Page

Background

- Born AD 570 in Mecca. Parents died early. Developed love of animals, e.g. cut a hole in cloak to avoid waking a sleeping kitten.
- Became a shepherd. In desert, visionary dreams foretold his future importance.
- At 25 became caravan leader and trader. Became disillusioned with moral and religious decay of Mecca, especially idol worship.
- Meditations led him to a vision of angel Gabriel in a cave. Gabriel explained that Muhammad was blessed and was to preach the message of God (Allah) to be revealed to him - even if he was illiterate.
- AD 610 began preaching. Taught followers love and brotherhood, to be kind, to love children, and respect elders, always to be truthful, not to harm each other, to lead a humble lifestyle, etc.
- First wife died AD 619. Rejected by Mecca because of his teaching. However, gained influence over Arabs who made annual pilgrimage to the Ka'bah in Mecca (an important building established by Abraham). Moved to Medina, 200 miles away.
- AD 622 became leading citizen, political and religious leader. (This became first year of Muslim calendar.) Proved himself to be great military leader in battles with the Meccans. AD 630 returned triumphant to Mecca on a camel.
- AD 632 completed his ministry. Returned to Medina. Died with head on lap of favourite wife, Aisha. Islam spread quickly through Arabia.
- Muslims greet each other with 'As salaamu alaykum'. (Peace be upon you.)
- The Qur'an, the Muslim holy book, is not a life of Muhammad, but a collection of Muhammad's recitations, collated by Abu Bakr, Muhammad's closest companion. Muslim belief is enshrined in the words 'There is no God but Allah and Muhammad is the messenger of Allah'. No records of miracles, acts of healing or resurrection, and no claims to divine authority by Muhammad.

Starting Points

- **What is known already?** Set context by using visuals, artefacts, visits to mosque, etc.
- **Tell his story.** Use the background information and the sequence of pictures. Explain that Muslims believe Muhammad to be a messenger, or the last in the line of great prophets from God.
- **The resource sheet.** Get the children to work in pairs. Cut out one set of the pictures between them. On a board/OHP list the key words:

  Love of animals, Shepherd, Visit by angel, Caravan leader, Worship of images, Gabriel speaks, Preaches love and peace, Military leader, Enters Mecca on camel, Aisha
- Each pair has to match the correct caption to the correct picture and sequence the pictures.

  A class collage or display could be made depicting key events in Muhammad's life.

Activities

Use each picture to discuss:

- **Love of animals.** Research stories about Muhammad's love for animals. Compare St Francis of Assisi (page 34). Which religions consider some animals sacred, e.g. Hindus?
- **Shepherd.** Jesus described himself as the 'Good Shepherd'. Discuss what this means.
- **The Angel's visit.** Compare Muhammad's annointment and Gabriel's visit to Mary.
- **Caravan leader.** Discuss the importance of camel caravans and trade in Muhammad's time and what Muhammad's work may have involved.
- **Worship of images.** No portraits or images of Muhammad or Allah are allowed in the Muslim faith. Discuss why.
- **Gabriel.** Dreams play a part in most world religions. Consider some of the dreams of the Old Testament prophets, e.g. Abraham, Isaiah, Ezekiel, Elijah.
- **Love and peace.** What are the qualities, demonstrated in Muhammad's teachings and lifestyle, that make him an important religious leader?
- **Military leadership.** Muhammad helped in fighting a holy war. Can there ever be a just cause to fight other human beings?
- **Triumphal entry by camel.** Jesus entered Jerusalem on a donkey. Muhammad entering Mecca on camel is a similar symbol of humility. Discuss this and emphasise the role of world faith leaders to 'serve'.
- **Aisha.** Discuss the importance of family relationships and what makes them special.

© 1993 Folens Ltd.

Muhammad

Jesus - Ideas Page

Background

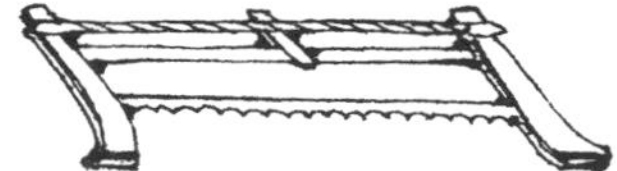

- Christians (followers of Christ) believe that Jesus is the Son of God, was born of the Virgin Mary and had no human father. *(Luke 2:1-7)*
- Became carpenter in Nazareth with earthly father Joseph. At twelve, Jesus amazed the temple elders in Jerusalem by being able to interpret the scriptures. *(Luke 2:39-52)*
- At thirty, baptised in River Jordan by John the Baptist. Received empowering of God's spirit. *(Luke 3:15-22)*
- Attracted crowds of ordinary people, enthralled by his teaching. Taught God's word in stories called parables. *(Luke 10:25-37)*
- Demonstrated the power of God through performing miracles. Compassion for sick and suffering. *(Matthew 8:1-4)*
- Displayed humility and willingness to serve others, e.g. washing disciples' feet. *(John 15:12-13)*
- Showed anger at those who exploited others, e.g. money changers at temple. *(Mark 11:15-19, 27-30)*
- Jews had long prophesied a 'Messiah' (a saviour) would free them from Roman domination. Triumphal welcome to Jerusalem, but Jesus entered on a donkey, demonstrating that he was a man of peace not a warrior king. *(Matthew 21:1-11)*
- Many couldn't accept his claim that he was the son of God. Priests felt threatened and plotted to have him killed. He was tried and sentenced to a cruel death on a cross. Viewed pain and suffering as part of his destiny. *(John 19:17-30)*
- Christians believe that after three days, Jesus rose again and went to heaven to be with his father. *(John 20:1-18)*
- Christians believe that Jesus sacrificed his life for them and that through him they can be forgiven and know God. His gospel (good news) of 'Love one another as I love you' provides a guide to living.

Starting Points

- **What did Jesus look like?** Explain that there are no contemporary pictorial records of Jesus. Ask the class to gather together as many different pictures of Jesus as possible. Discuss them. How do different artists portray him? What characteristics does each portray?
- **The story of Jesus.** Looking at each picture and using Bible references and other reference material, discuss his story.
- **Using the resource sheet.** Get the children to work in pairs. Cut out one set of pictures between them. On a board/ OHP list the key words:
  Nativity, Temple, Baptism, Good Samaritan, Healing, Humility and service, Anger, Entry on donkey, Crucifixion, Resurrection.
- Each pair has to match the correct caption to each picture, and sequence them. A class display could depict key events in Christ's life.

Activities

Use each picture to discuss:

- **The nativity.** How much else do the children know of the Christmas story? Refer to biblical sources.
- **The temple.** For Christians, the Holy Bible is believed to be the Word of God. How much do the children know about the Bible? Discuss its composition and contents.
- **Baptism.** Jesus was baptized in the waters of the Jordan. Discuss the symbolism of water in religions.
- **The Good Samaritan.** Use this parable as a way to discuss examples of communities or nations failing to put 'Love thy Neighbour' into practice.
- **Healing.** Jesus used healing and miracles to point people to the power of God. Talk about the example given *(Matthew 8: 1-4)*. Find examples of others in the Bible.
- **Humility.** Jesus, the Son of God, was prepared to wash the feet of his disciples (an accepted and necessary act of courtesy in a very dusty country). What does this tell us about the man? How do we show respect for others?
- **Anger.** Jesus is often shown as meek and gentle. However, on this occasion he showed considerable anger. Why? What does this show us about him?
- **Entry to Jerusalem.** The Jews thought differently about the coming Messiah (saviour). Jesus wanted to show he was a man of peace. In what ways did Jesus look and act differently from the expected 'warrior king'?
- **Crucifixion.** The cross has become a powerful symbol of Christianity. Discuss where we see crosses today.
- **Resurrection.** Why do eggs at Easter symbolise the possibility of new life?

© 1993 Folens Ltd.

Jesus

© 1993 Folens Ltd. This page may be photocopied for classroom use only

Gandhi - Ideas Page

Background

Einstein: 'Generations to come will scarce believe that such a one as this, ever in flesh and blood, walked upon this earth.'

- Born 1869 into wealthy Hindu family. Arranged marriage to 13 year old. Rebelled as teenager, e.g. stole from father. Saw error of ways and confessed. Forgiven with loving embrace.
- Studied law in England. Worked as lawyer in South Africa. Rampant racism, e.g. was not allowed to travel in same train carriage as whites, called a 'coolie' and kicked off train.
- Fought to improve lot of coloured population through non-violent means. Used legal skill, e.g. fought and won case of a black labourer who was beaten and ill-treated by white owner.
- Boer War, formed Ambulance Corps to help the wounded. The massacre of Zulus in 1906 by British convinced him that only way to live decently was to practise 'ahimsa' (non-violence to all living creatures) and to fight injustice and violence with the power of truth and love ('satyagraha').
- Returned to India 1915. Tried to unite Hindus and Muslims. Adopted a policy of non-cooperation with British (Indians vital as labour force and market). 1919 General Strike and day of prayer. Imprisoned for this.
- 1930 Salt March. British imposed tax on all salt - no making, selling, eating salt not imported from Britain. Gandhi led 24 day trek to Arabian Sea. Publicly picked up and ate a grain of salt. Hundreds of peaceful demonstrators clubbed - refused to retaliate. World opinion outraged. 1931 called to London for talks. Gradual move to self-government and independence.
- 1947 part of India split away to form Muslim state of Pakistan - much bloodshed.
- 1948 Gandhi was shot by a Hindu fanatic.
- Gandhi prepared to stand up for beliefs. Imprisoned for 2 338 days in total. Fasted almost till death to persuade people of his seriousness.
- Believed: you should love all creatures; everyone is equal in the face of God; in power of meditation - taking time to listen to a silent 'inner' voice; truth was whatever you felt in your heart to be morally correct and good; in non-violence; in religious tolerance; all religions are different roads converging on same point. Called 'Mahatma' which means 'great soul'.

Starting Points

- **Tell his story.** Use the background information and the pictures to take the children through the life of Gandhi.
- **Using the resource sheet.** Children work in pairs with one set of pictures between them. On board/OHP list the key words:

  Marriage, Forgiveness, Arriving in London, Lawyer, Racism, Defending the exploited, Ambulance Corps, Salt March, Independence, Assassination.

  Each pair has to match the correct caption to each picture and sequence them, re-telling the story as they do so.
- **A great man.** Write out the tribute by Einstein and discuss. Talk about the meaning of 'Mahatma' ('great soul'). Draw pictures of Gandhi dressed in a simple loin cloth. What does his simple choice of clothes tell us about the man?

Activities

Use each picture to discuss:

- **Marriage.** Discuss experience and knowledge of different faiths' marriage ceremonies. The whole issue of 'arranged' marriages provides a lively topic for discussion.
- **Forgiveness.** Was Gandhi's father right to do what he did? Compare with Jesus' final words on the cross 'Father forgive them for they know not what they do'.
- **Arriving in London.** Discuss the issues of dress and appearance. Explore the concept of 'When in Rome, do as the Romans do'.
- **Lawyer.** Follow on from last point and compare how Gandhi is now dressed! Why?
- **Racism.** Children could collect and bring in newspaper cuttings of items highlighting racial conflict around the world. Is racism still prevalent in our society? If so, why?
- **Defending the exploited.** Caste system - 'the biggest single stain on the Hindu faith'. Consider Gandhi's belief that everyone, whatever status, is equal in the face of God.
- **Ambulance Corps.** How could forming an Ambulance Corps be squared with his belief in *ahimsa*?
- **Salt March.** Why was this such an important point in Gandhi's fight against injustice?
- **Independence.** Explore the reasons why some countries seek to rule over others.
- **Assassination.** Reflect on the personal sacrifices that inspirational figures are prepared to make for their beliefs.

Gandhi

Martin Luther King - Ideas Page

Background

- Although slavery in the USA was abolished by the time Martin Luther was born in 1929, much 'slave mentality' still prevailed. Even recently laws still discriminated against blacks, e.g. schools, buses segregated in some states of USA.
- Martin Luther King studied hard. Could have become a lawyer but chose to become a Baptist minister (like his father). Study of Bible gave him strong belief in justice, equality and rights of the marginalised. His hero was Gandhi and the passive resistance movement in India.
- Rosa Parks incident (Montgomery, Alabama, 1955) - Rosa jailed for refusing to give up her bus seat to a white man. King's response: 'If we are not allowed to use the buses freely with the whites then we will not use them at all.' For 382 days no blacks used buses until law changed. Martin Luther organised 'sit ins', marches, peaceful demonstrations. Never met violence with violence.
- Martin Luther was persuasive speaker. Got public opinion behind him. Awarded Nobel Peace Prize in 1964.
- One of his famous speeches summarises beliefs:
  'I have a dream. I have a dream that my four children will one day live in a nation where they will not be judged by the colour of their skin but by the content of their character.'
- Martin Luther assassinated in 1968. Symbolically, coffin drawn by mules.

Starting Points

- **Yin and Yang.** Ask for ideas about what it could mean. Discuss. Explain that it symbolises a Chinese philosophical belief that the Earth's energy forces are in perfect harmony and are interdependent.
- **Complete the picture.** Colour black all the spaces numbered with a one on the resource sheet. Discuss the complementary nature and the harmony of the black and white. When does the complete picture emerge?

Activities

- **Tell his story.** Use the background information to tell his story. Children could do some research to see what else they could find out about Martin Luther.
- **Unjust treatment.** Ask for personal examples of unjust treatment. Discuss how you feel at these times. Discuss fairness and justice of these situations.
- **Different groups - different treatment .** Discuss justification for different categories of people being treated differently, e.g. the elderly, the physically handicapped, children. Think of some examples.
- **Courage and cowardice.** Think of examples of both from the life story of Martin Luther.
- **Beliefs.** What did Martin Luther believe in? What were the origins of his beliefs? For example, the teaching of the Bible and Christ's life. (The Good Samaritan is a classic tale of racism.)
- **Truth hurts.** Standing up for your beliefs sometimes makes you unpopular. Why was this the case with Martin Luther?
- **Might makes right?** Children often solve problems in the playground by bullying and aggression. Ask for opinions on Martin Luther methods of non-violence. Is violence ever justified?
- **What's in a name?** - A *king* is a leader. An appropriate name for the man? Ask the children to find out why they were given their names. Do their forenames or surnames mean anything?
- **I have a dream ...** What is the children's dream of an ideal world? Make a list of ideas.
- **X rays.** X rays can 'see through' the surface colour of our skin and see what's underneath. Look at some X rays, discuss anatomy and bone structures. Make the point that it is not the colour of our skin which is important but what we are like on the inside. Ask children: What would you say are your best qualities? Would your friends agree?
- **Negro spirituals** tell us a lot about the lives of negro slaves. Listen to some and discuss the lyrics, e.g. *Swing low, Sweet Chariot.*

© 1993 Folens Ltd.

Martin Luther King

Colour black all the spaces numbered (1) and talk about what picture emerges. At what point did you realise what the picture was?

© 1993 Folens Ltd. This page may be photocopied for classroom use only

Lord Shaftesbury - Ideas Page

Background

- **19th Century:** unprecedented industrial growth. No organised protection for workers. Atrocious conditions in factories, mills and mines. Long hours for minimal pay.
- Economic necessity forced parents to send children to work. Children often started at eight years old. Down the coal mines and in factories children as young as four were used. Worked in excess of sixty hours a week. Beatings and strappings regular feature.
- **Lord Shaftesbury:** typical of small, active group of philanthropic Victorians campaigning for social changes.
- **Born 1801** into wealthy Christian family. As a child witnessed the poverty of a pauper's funeral. Determined him to live life working to help poor. Believed God called him to do this.
- **Became MP in 1826.** Gave power and influence to change things. Became a champion of the cause of oppressed. Successfully harnessed public opinion. Patience, persistence and continued pressure brought gradual success despite many disappointments and failures.
- **1842** Mines Act. Forbade employment of women and girls and boys under ten down coal mines.
- **1844** Began Ragged Schools Union. Collected money and set up very basic form of schooling for poor, often homeless, children.
- **1847** Ten Hours Act limited the working day of women and young people. (NB not men!)
- **Died 1885.** Statue of Eros in Piccadilly erected in memory of him and his achievements.

Starting Points

- **Social Context.** Read excerpts from Dickens' *Oliver Twist*, Kingsley's *Water Babies*. Use film or video. Refer to historical sources for illustrations and background. Explore children's responses to the way workers were treated, especially children - through writing stories, diaries, discussion and role play.
- **Play the game** from the resource sheet.
- **Lord Shaftesbury.** Use background notes (and any other available information) to tell his story. Be creative interpreting the bare facts. Dramatise, e.g. empathising with different people's feelings - the workers or Shaftesbury, imagining the angry exchanges in parliament.

Activities

- **His motives.** Explain that Shaftesbury came from a wealthy, privileged background, immune from suffering and hardship. Why was he prepared to spend life fighting, continually harassed and facing opposition, prepared to suffer huge disappointments? Consider some of the influences and how they could have affected him, e.g. the impact of the pauper's funeral, his Christian background (look at some examples of Christian teaching, e.g. 'love thy neighbour' as shown in parable of Good Samaritan).
- **His qualities.** Ask children to suggest some of the qualities that characterised Shaftesbury, e.g. patience, persistence, ability to face and overcome huge disappointments, commitment, concern for underprivileged, compassion, duty, good communicator. Try to tease out what these involve and consider how Shaftesbury demonstrated them.
- **Points of view.** Discuss the fact that different people have different value systems and attitudes towards things. Bring out the point that in all relationships it is important to understand and listen to different points of view before making judgements or decisions. Talk about examples of this in school or home life. Shaftesbury met great opposition from some factory and mill owners. The bosses had a very different agenda from Shaftesbury. Try to imagine what their motives were. What were they interested in?
- **Other philanthropists.** Research other philanthropists and consider what made them act in the way they did.
- **Exploitation.** Consider what the word *exploitation* means. What is needed to keep a home running smoothly? What jobs are involved? Consider whether the tasks are fairly distributed in our homes. Are there ways in which we could each make a better contribution?

Lord Shaftesbury

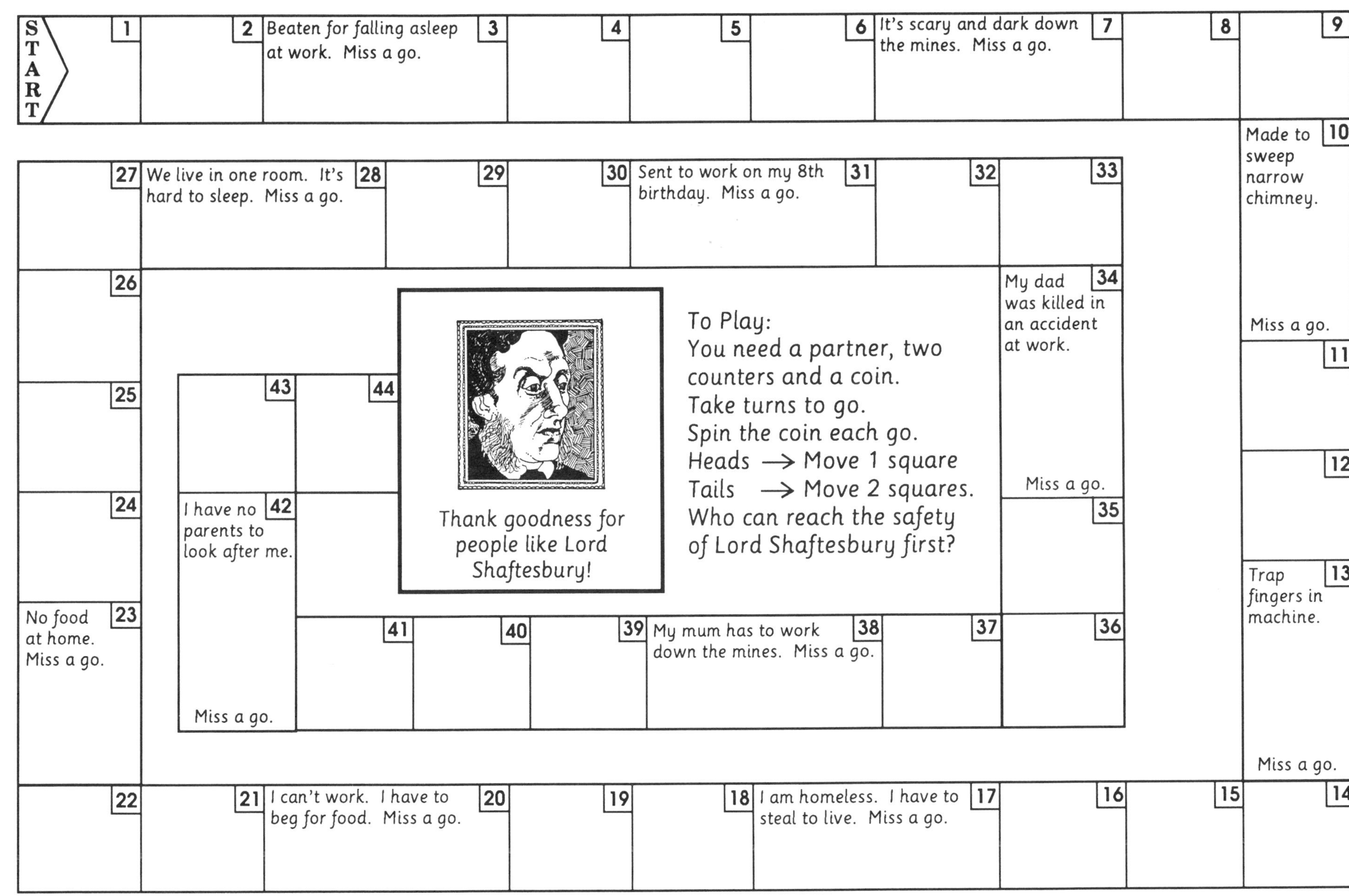

© Folens Ltd. This page may be photocopied for classroom use only

Helen Keller - Ideas Page

Background

- Born in USA 1880. 1882 struck by mystery illness. Lost her sight and hearing. Inability to communicate made her hit out in anger and despair. Became virtually uncontrollable.
- Anne Sullivan, teacher, came to live and work with Helen. Anne bore brunt of Helen's violent outbursts. Won Helen's confidence with very firm, but affectionate, approach.
- Dramatic changes soon began to appear. Helen began to show a sweet, loving nature; became obedient child.
- Helen was an intelligent child. Anne helped Helen learn to express herself by using the hand alphabet. Helen made the dramatic discovery that everything had a name. (WATER was associated with the cold liquid that gushed from the pump.)
- Helen learned to read and write, using raised letters and Braille. Helen at last able to begin to lead an ordinary life.
- News of her dramatic triumph over adversity spread. She even learnt how to speak, and successfully attended college.
- As an adult worked tirelessly for women's rights, the handicapped and the poor, against child labour, against capital punishment. She spoke out forcefully for what she believed in, made films, wrote books, gave concerts, raised money in all sorts of ways.
- Helen died in 1968 after an inspirational life of determination and perseverance against all the odds, and of altruism and selfless devotion to others.

Starting Points

- **Thinking about blindness and deafness.** Do any of the children know anyone who is blind or deaf? What problems do they experience in day-to-day life? What must it be like to be blind or deaf?
- **Help for the blind and deaf.** What sorts of things can be done to help people with these handicaps? e.g. Braille, hearing aids, guide dogs. Use the resource sheet to discuss the use of the manual alphabet and Braille.

Activities

- **Bad behaviour.** Helen said she was 'a wild, destructive little animal' as a young child. Try to explain why this was. What sort of things would she have done?
- **Bad manners.** Helen's table manners must have been pretty awful as a young child. Rules are normally written to ensure people behave properly. Make up some 'Reverse Rules for Behaviour at the Table' - just for fun!
- **Trust.** Anne Sullivan's first priority was to establish trust with Helen. What do children understand by trust? What sort of people do they trust? What qualities do they have?
- **Communicating without words.** Try communicating some words or a simple message to someone using the manual alphabet and Braille. Discuss experiences together. How easy or hard was it? What were the problems? How frustrating was it? Why?
- **Seeing the light.** Other dramatic examples could be studied when characters *saw the light* and were transformed from darkness into understanding. For example, St Paul's Damascus experience when the 'scales dropped from his eyes'. *(Acts 9)*
- **What did Helen believe?** Helen looked forward to a time when there would be 'but one family, the human race; one law, peace; one need, harmony; one taskmaster, God'. Discuss what we can learn about Helen from this quotation.
- **Helen's adult life.** How did Helen's beliefs influence the way she lived her life? What sort of things did she do? Why?
- **Drama.** Aspects of Helen's story lend themselves well to dramatisation, e.g. Anne teaching Helen the manual alphabet, etc.
- **The senses.** The topic of Helen Keller has many obvious links with the importance of our senses. Lots of interesting science work could be introduced along with it.

© 1993 Folens Ltd.

Helen Keller

Here are two ways that Helen Keller used to communicate.

- *Send messages to each other in the two alphabets.*
- *How difficult is it to learn how to use them?*

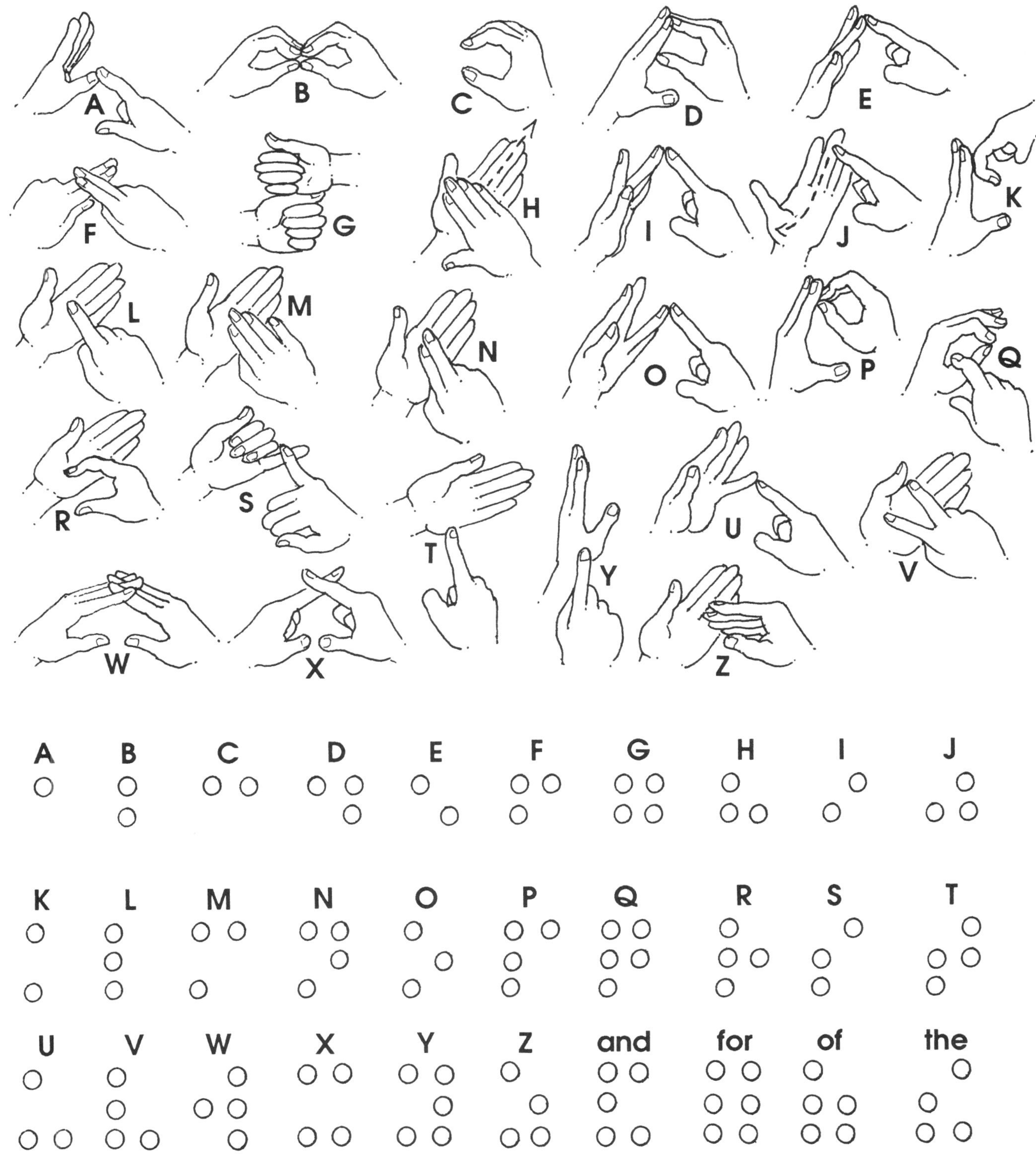

© 1993 Folens Ltd.
This page may be photocopied for classroom use only

Cliff Richard - Ideas Page

Background

- Born 1940, in India (while his father working there). Returned UK 1947. Left school and worked as a clerk.
- '50s saw rise of Rock 'n' Roll. Cliff modelled himself on Elvis Presley. Formed rock group 1958 - the Shadows. Quickly became popular. Has had over 100 hit singles and fifty albums!
- Consolidated early career with acting in films. In 1986 led to major role in sci-fi stage show ***Time***, which dealt with world's shortcomings, need to live in harmony, of being loving, caring and wise.
- At twenty-five in spite of all his success, felt there was something missing in his life. After a lot of thinking, became a Christian.
- Enormous temptations of 'show biz' hard to resist, e.g. money, status, lifestyle. Wanted to live his life true to his beliefs. Believed Jesus wanted him to continue pop career doing what he did best, and to show the love of Christ through his lifestyle and example. Combined pop with gospel concerts, using his popularity as a means to enable him to tell people about his beliefs. Never forces his views on others, prefers to let his life and example speak for itself.
- Enthusiastically supports Christian work helping the needy wherever they happen to be, and travels tirelessly throughout world to do so. Gives freely of his time and money for this purpose.
- Believes in importance of being 'right' inside (spiritually) and outside (physically). Believes in living life to the full but also in living a healthy lifestyle, not drinking or smoking and getting enough sleep and exercise. Convinced of the importance of loving relationships with family and friends.

Starting Points

- Ask children to bring in videos, photos, information, records of Cliff Richard. Share findings together.
- Get the children to write their own mini biography of Cliff. Perhaps it could be written and illustrated in comic strip form.
- Introduce the 'Cliffhanger' game. Explain that whoever we are, whether famous or just ordinary, we all have to face many ups and downs in life - all part of learning more about ourselves, the world in which we live, who we are and where we are going. For many people, like Cliff Richard, having a firm set of beliefs and strong faith is a great help in life, sustaining them and giving them a set of principles to live their lives by.
- **Rules.** Throw two dice each turn. Move the counter the difference between the two throws (e.g. if a 6 and 1 are thrown, move 5 places). A throw of two of anything results in no move at all.

Activities

- **Make a collage** of famous stars from the entertainment world. How do these people influence our lives? Is their influence always good and healthy?
- **All that glitters is not gold!** Discuss some of the exciting things about being a pop star. Discuss some of the disadvantages and possible dangers wealth can bring.
- **What's so special?** List five things which are special about Cliff Richard. Share them with a partner and listen to partner's ideas. Pick the five most important and together come up with a final list of five.
- **Following Christ.** Cliff believes that we can learn a lot by studying the example of Jesus. Christ showed care and concern for the suffering and those in need. Read some examples found in the Gospel stories. Discuss the importance of not just talking about these things but living them out and doing something practical about them. Talk about the ways Cliff Richard does this.
- **Care of the environment.** Cliff Richard believes that God gave us the world to live in and it is our responsibility to look after it. Take this as an opportunity to talk about what we as individuals, and collectively as a group, can do in a practical sense. Devise a campaign.
- **Healthy in body and spirit.** Being 'right' with God is obviously important for Cliff. He combines this with a concern for his physical welfare too. Talk about the benefits of a healthy lifestyle. Make some posters on a Good Health theme showing some do's and don'ts.

© Folens Ltd.

Cliff Hanger?

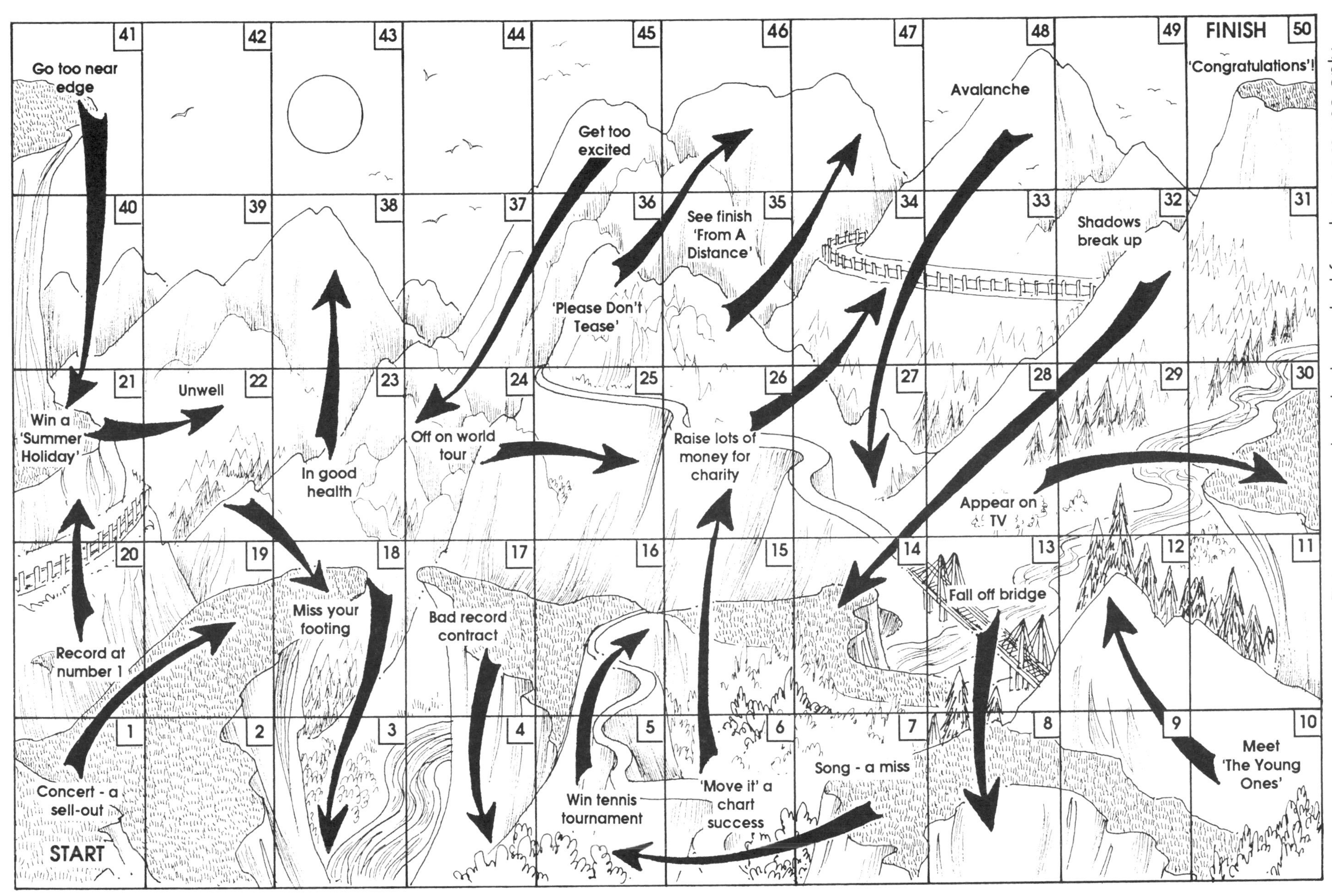

© Folens Ltd. This page may be photocopied for classroom use only

Mother Teresa - Ideas Page

Background

'Many great people have trod this earth, but very few of these have been good people. Mother Teresa is good as well as great.' M Desai, India's Prime Minister, 1970.

- Born Agnes Bojaxhiu in 1910, Serbia (formerly part of Yugoslavia). Became a nun in Ireland 1928. Changed her name to Sister Mary Teresa.
- Sent to India (Calcutta) - 'indescribable poverty' and appalling living conditions, breeding sickness and death. Worked in clinics, hospitals and schools. Called 'Ma' meaning 'Mother'.
- 1946 travelling to Darjeeling by train, 'when I heard the voice of God ... I was sure it was God's voice. I was certain he was calling me. The message was clear: I must leave the convent to help the poor by living among them.'
- Established the Missionaries of Charity in 1948. No-one was turned away by the Missionaries of Charity. The sisters vowed not to own possessions or have wealth of their own, but to give everything they had to helping the poor. Home for the Dying Destitute founded in 1952 - a place where such people could end their days with dignity and care. Home for abandoned babies founded in 1955. 1957 Mother Teresa set up a clinic for lepers.
- Nobel Peace Prize in 1979. Her response to this was typical - 'Personally I am unworthy. I accept it in the name of the poor.'
- 'The sheer goodness which shines through Mother Teresa's life and work can only inspire humility, wonder and admiration - and what more is there to be said when the deeds speak so loudly for themselves?' The Duke of Edinburgh, 1973.

Starting Points

- **New Year resolutions.** What does the word 'resolution' mean? Why do people make them? Jot down a few things that children would like to try hard to do in the future. How likely is it that they could maintain these for a lifetime?
- **'Spread love everywhere you go: first of all in your own home.'** List a few ideas to adopt this resolution and discuss them. What would the world be like if we all tried to stick to this resolution?
- **A very special person.** Children should research and tell her story. Use the photocopiable page and write as many reasons as you can around her picture to explain why you think Mother Teresa could be called ***special***.

Activities

- **Count Your Blessings.** Make a list of ten or so things or people, that children are thankful for. Perhaps this could be turned into a prayer.
- **Money, money, money!** What do the children like to spend their pocket money on? If they suddenly became rich over night how would they spend their money? Contrast statements about the Missionaries of Charity, drawing out the sort of sacrifices Mother Teresa makes: 'We do not accept anything whatsoever from our parents, friends or benefactors for our personal use. Whatever is given to us is handed over for the common use of the community or for our work.' The only possessions the sisters are allowed to have are: two saris, one pair of sandals, underwear, a rope girdle, a crucifix, a mattress and a bucket to wash in.
- **Service.** Think of people in our community who offer a service in some way, e.g. the lollipop lady or man, the person who delivers the milk. Mother Teresa offered her whole life to serve 'the King of the world'. Try to think through what this might mean.
- **Prayer.** Discuss the concept of prayer as 'talking to God'. Do we have to use 'special' language to talk to God? Is it possible for God to talk to us?
- **Humility.** Read her response to winning the Nobel Peace Prize again. What does this tell about the sort of person Mother Teresa is? What words could children use to describe her?
- **Interview.** Imagine children were asked to interview Mother Teresa. What questions would they ask her? Write down a few questions. What answers do they think they might get?

© 1993 Folens Ltd.

Mother Teresa

People think that Mother Teresa is a very special person. Do some research about her life and write around the picture reasons why you think she is so special.

© 1993 Folens Ltd.

This page may be photocopied for classroom use only

Florence Nightingale - Ideas Page

Background

- Born 1820 - wealthy family.
- When 16, she came across a sheepdog that had a broken leg - helped shepherd mend the leg. Convinced she should be a nurse.
- Parents felt nursing was not a 'suitable' job for a Victorian lady.
- Hospitals at this time were squalid , overcrowded and disease-ridden. Antiseptics and anaesthetics were unknown. Nurses were untrained.
- Felt she had been called by God to serve. Without her parents' consent, went to train as a nurse.
- 1854 Crimean War.
- Florence sent out to organise the care of the sick and wounded. Hospital at Scutari dirty, soldiers crammed everywhere and given little attention, medication, etc.
- Soldiers called her an angel and the 'Lady of the Lamp'.
- British public took her to their hearts. Queen Victoria publicly thanked her. Gave her a brooch, engraved with words 'Blessed are the merciful'.

Starting Points

- **Discuss the job of nurses today.** Consider some of the motives nurses may have for going into the profession.
- **World need.** Discuss some current situations and the work of individuals and humanitarian organisations who offer support and help at the point of need. Discuss our reactions to such situations. Is it possible for us as individuals to help in any way?
- **The Florence Nightingale Story.** Using the background information children tell the story of Florence in their own words. Cut out, discuss and sequence the set of pictures. They could then write a simple caption for each picture or re-tell the story in their own words.

Activities

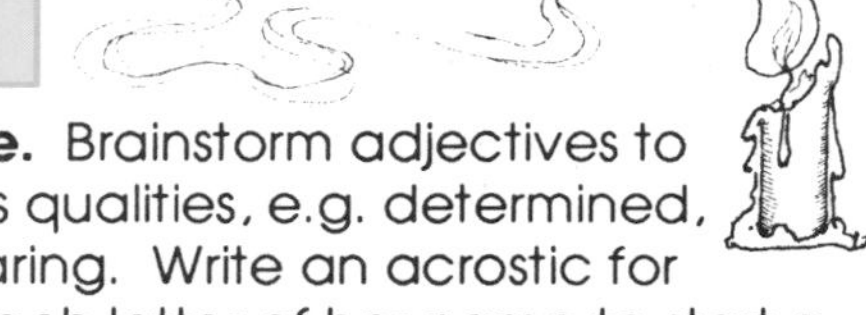

- **Describing Florence.** Brainstorm adjectives to describe Florence's qualities, e.g. determined, compassionate, caring. Write an acrostic for FLORENCE, using each letter of her name to start a sentence or a phrase which tells something of her character or life.
- **Principles bring pain.** Sometimes Florence stuck to her beliefs even though it brought her into conflict with others, e.g. her parents. Is this always a good thing? Should you be prepared to listen to other people's point of view?
- **Turning point.** Meeting the sheepdog was one incident that was a turning point for Florence. It helped confirm her belief that nursing was what she had to do. Research other people whose lives were changed by particular incidents. Have there been really significant moments in any of the children's lives which stick in their minds as being very important for some reason?
- **Know your place.** Florence's parents thought that nursing was 'not suitable for a young Victorian lady'. Discuss the changing role of women in society. Compare the view of her parents with the situation today. What things might her parents have considered suitable? Make a list of jobs which are typically carried out by men or by women. Are we as guilty today of stereotyping as the Victorians?
- **Angels.** The word 'angel' literally means 'sent from God'. In what way was this an appropriate name for Florence? In the Bible, angels are often sent as messengers from God. Find some examples of angels appearing and discuss their significance.
- **Other Victorian women.** Many other Victorian women broke the mould because of their religious convictions, e.g. Elizabeth Fry, Mary Seacole. Research the lives of some of these.
- **Drama.** Florence's story is full of incidents suitable for dramatising. Imagine some situations:
  a) A newspaper reporter, telling the story of Florence during the Crimean War.
  b) One of the soldiers in the hospital. How would you view the coming of Florence?
  c) Florence herself. Imagine you were writing a diary. You could write about your first impressions of the hospital; the soldiers' conditions and your attempts to improve things; your meeting with Queen Victoria.

© Folens Ltd.

Florence Nightingale

Tell the story of Florence Nightingale's life.

- Fill in the speech bubbles with what you think the characters might have said.

© 1993 Folens Ltd. This page may be photocopied for classroom use only

Francis of Assisi - **Ideas Page**

Background

- St Francis is partly remembered today as a very special person who cared for people, the environment and the animals that live in it.
- Born in Assissi, Italy 1182 into a wealthy family.
- Sought adventure in the army. One day came across an old soldier begging by the roadside. Recognised the man as someone he had once known from a wealthy family who had fallen on hard times. Overwhelmed with pity. Gave his fine clothes to the beggar because 'This man is my brother'.
- Began to be troubled by dreams. Realised that he had lived a selfish life thinking only of his own comfort and pleasure, and that money was no guarantee of happiness. Francis believed that God was telling him to get up and help the poor.
- Left home and travelled the country, sheltering wherever he could, begging for food; gave away his own clothes and money to anyone in need. His family did not understand.
- Francis believed that the world had become a greedy and selfish place in which few people cared or thought about others. Believed God was asking him to help rebuild a church which had 'no walls but the air, no roof but the sky - it was here, there and everywhere'. God was talking about the world in which we live - not just a building!
- God would provide for his needs. Wherever he went, he told people about God's love for them and the world. Gradually built up a group of followers.
- Francis demonstrated his power over animals and his concern for them. He saw them all as an important part of God's creation. He died in 1226.

Starting Points

- **Tell the story.** Use the background information to help you tell the story. Explain that St Francis was a real person who lived a long time ago.
- Do the children believe the story? How could it be proved that Francis existed? Does the fact that Francis lived in the past make the story less valuable, important or interesting?
- **Concern for animals.** Complete the resource sheet. Talk about the style of the sheet, the illuminated letters, the layout, the way the illustrations support the theme of the page.
- Discuss the ways in which Francis showed a concern for animals and his motivation. Discuss the work of animal welfare today: the RSPCA, whaling, etc.

Activities

- **Creative interpretation through drama and role play.**
  - Francis speaks to the beggar. Think of it from both points of view. What would each have seen, thought, said, felt?
  - The Family. What would their reactions to Francis' change of lifestyle be? What would they have said or thought? What would they have said to Francis to try to dissuade him? How would Francis have tried to explain what he was doing?
  - Francis preaching the Gospel. What would the different reactions to Francis have been when he told people about God? What would people have said or done?
- **Happiness is ...** Ask the children to write down and share their thoughts on what makes them happy as a simple list poem.
- **Concern for others.** Francis' concern was with helping the poor. Who are the poor locally? globally? Francis wanted to help the poor in a very practical way. List ways children could help one group of poor practically.
- **Concern for the environment.** Francis cared passionately for the environment ('God's creation'). Decorate and design a poster like the one on animals using this verse:

The mountain and river
The sea and the sky
The sun and the stars
The bird and butterfly
To Francis, God was the Father
Of him and all others
The flowers were his sisters,
And trees were his brothers.

- Raise questions and concerns about our responsibilities towards the Earth and its resources and the future of our planet. Work on practical situations - conservation, pollution, recycling.

© 1993 Folens Ltd.

Francis of Assisi

Here is a poem about Francis of Assisi. Talk about St Francis and then write a third verse for the poem. Make the sheet look as attractive as possible for display in your class.

he family of Francis
Were not as another's.
The birds were his sisters
The beasts were his brothers.

hese were his names
For animals great and small.
To Francis, God was Father
Of him and them all.

© 1993 Folens Ltd.
This page may be photocopied for classroom use only

Yusuf Islam - Ideas Page

Background

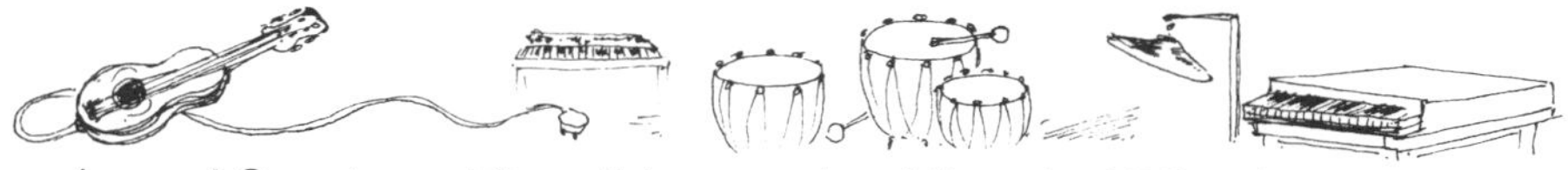

- **1948** Born as Steven Georgiou, of Greek and Swedish parents. Attended RC primary school.
- **1965** Went into music business as Cat Stevens. Had many hits, e.g. *Morning Has Broken.* Sold over 15 million LPs. Showed love of humanity. Supported charities and organisations like UNESCO.
- **1972** Visited Marrakesh in Morocco. Heard people singing to praise God. Began a profound change in his life. Previously had only thought of music as something to entertain others.
- **1973-75** Became disenchanted with trappings of fame. No longer satisfied him. Began search for inner peace and the true purpose of life. 'I was walking somewhere but didn't know where.'
- **1975** Brother returned from Middle East with a Qur'an (Muslim holy book.) Cat read it avidly. 'A feeling of belonging ran through me. I was a stream that had found its ocean!'
- **1977** Decided to serve God full time. Gave up 'showbiz'. Became a Muslim as Yusuf (after Joseph the prophet) and Islam (means submission to the will of God) as a statement of his faith.
- **1983** Founded Islamia Primary School in London specially for Muslim children. (School uses same curriculum as state schools but also has classes in Arabic, the Qur'an and Islam.) Struggled with Government to get state funding on same basis as Christian and Jewish schools.
- **Present** Active in promoting Islam.

Starting Points

- **Challenge** the children to see what they can discover about Cat Stevens the pop star. Ask their parents and other adults about him. See if they can find any of his records or pictures of him.
- **Sing** '*Morning Has Broken*' in assembly.
- **Tell his story.** Look at the resource sheet. Explain that it shows some aspects of Yusuf's life. Talk about the way life is a little like a continuous moving belt, developing and changing as it goes along. Use the background notes to tell his story.
- **Using the resource sheet.** Ask children in small groups or pairs to recall and retell what they can of the story. They could be asked to write simple captions on the 'belt' regarding each illustration.

Activities

- **What's in a name?** Why do we have them? What makes them special? How are they chosen? Yusuf changed his name once when he became a pop star and once when he became a Muslim. Why did he do this? Consider the meaning of the name *Islam.* Yusuf is a religious name. Do any of the children have names originating from holy books?
- **Life as a pop star.** Discuss some of the good things about being a pop star. What makes pop stars 'special'? Explore why Cat Stevens might have become disenchanted with the world of pop. What did he mean when he said he was *walking somewhere but didn't know where*?
- **A God-shaped hole.** Someone once said that in every one of us there is a God-shaped hole. What could this mean? How do people find out about God? Consider the effect on Cat Stevens of finding the Qur'an.
- **Sacrifice and service.** What did following God mean to Cat Stevens? What was he prepared to give up? How did his life change? In what ways has he served Islam? Compare Cat's experiences with those of Cliff Richard. (See page 28.)
- **School.** Why did Yusuf establish a Muslim school? Discuss the idea of separating children on grounds of religion. What are the advantages and disadvantages?
- **Our life stories.** Use the resource sheet for children to think about their own lives so far. What major events have there been in them? Have there been any big changes? What particularly important things in their (and their family's lives) can they remember? A 'Story of my Life' picture could be produced using the same 'moving belt' idea.
- **The future.** Yusuf Islam's life story is still unfolding. Is it possible to predict what the future holds? Consider some people's claims to tell the future by gazing into crystal balls and the stars (horoscopes).

© 1993 Folens Ltd.

Yusuf Islam

Everyone's life is like a continuous moving belt. Show this by putting aspects of Yusuf Islam's life on the correct belts.

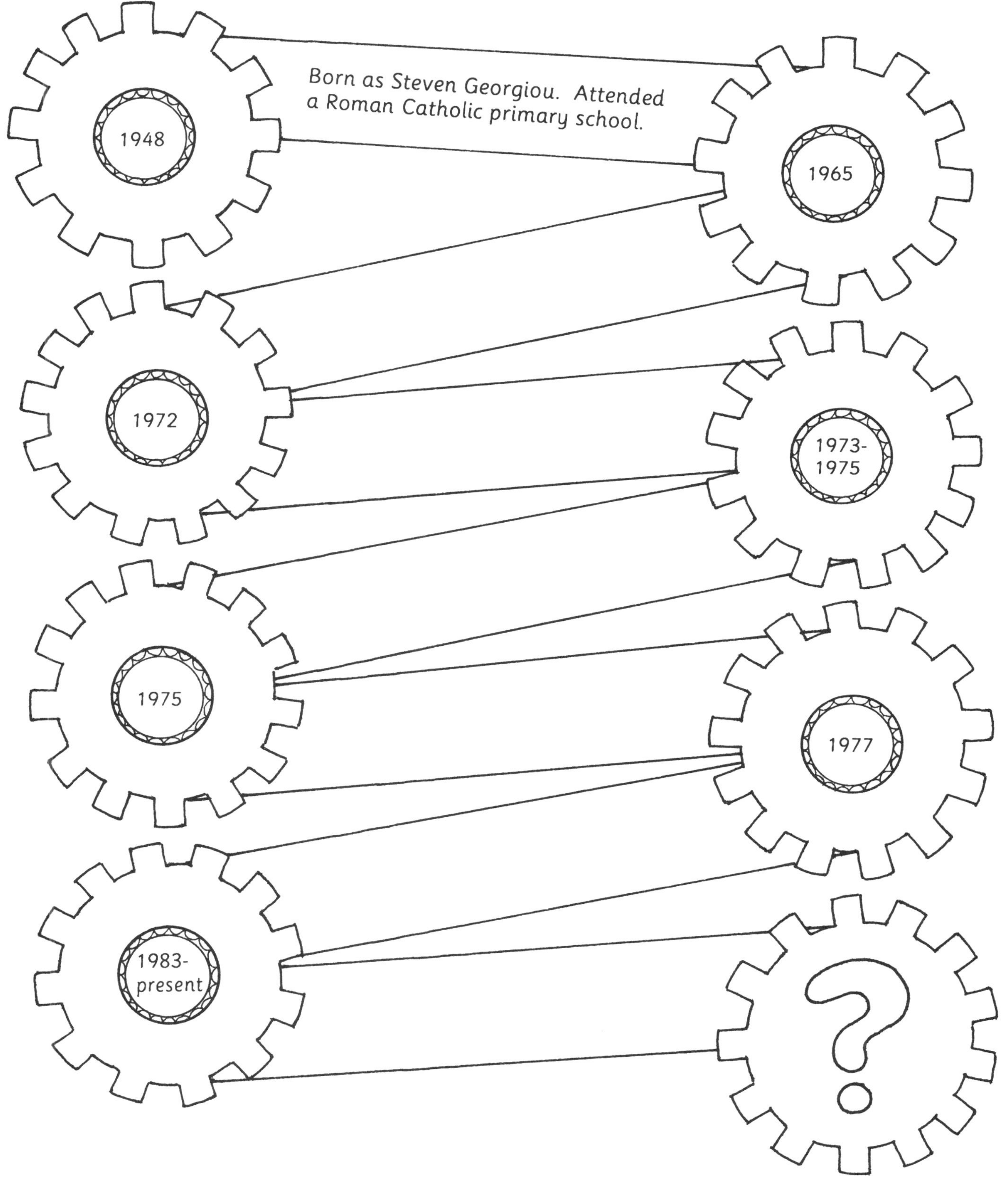

© 1993 Folens Ltd. This page may be photocopied for classroom use only

Religious Leaders in the Community - Ideas Page

Aim

The aim of this theme is to raise awareness of the role of religious leaders in the community and explore what makes them special.

Starting Points

- **Developing a concept of 'religious communities'.** Ask children to bring in costumes, artefacts, photographs, etc. relating to key religious ceremonies, celebrations, festivals, places of worship they attend. Children from brownie, cub, Boy's Brigade groups, etc. could come in their uniforms. Ask them to talk about the things they have brought in and what they represent. Draw out the fact that within the community as a whole there are other communities or groups of people who hold religious beliefs of different sorts.
- **Religious meeting places.** Where do different religious groups meet in the local community? Can they be located on a local map? Do any of the children go to them? What are the meeting places like? Draw pictures and plans to show how they look inside and outside. What happens there?
- **Religious leaders.** Research the names and responsibilities of various religious leaders. Are they men or women? (This could lead to some interesting discussions!) Discuss some possible reasons for religious groups usually having a leader. Why are they important?
- **Invite a religious leader in.** Ideally, asking a local religious leader to come into school and discuss his/her work, is a good way to stimulate interest and introduce many of the concepts and ideas to be covered.

Activities

- **Dressing differently.** Discuss why cubs and brownies wear special uniforms. Why do the police? Discuss whether you can sometimes tell the job someone does by the clothes they wear. Can you recognise the religious leaders in your community by the clothes they wear? Look at the resource sheet showing the way different religious leaders sometimes dress. Compare the ways they look and the clothes they wear.
- **What do religious leaders do?** Brainstorm suggestions about what special responsibilities, duties, jobs the religious leaders might have or do. Record the ideas as a wall display.
- **Classifying aspects of the job.** One useful way of classifying these responsibilities and duties is in a table:

Administrative	Pastoral	Religious

Discuss what each of the words mean, with examples. This could be done as a class or in small groups. Are the headings sufficient? Should there be any others?

- **Qualities.** Ask the children to discuss and record special qualities they think all religious leaders need, e.g. the ability to listen, care, share, understand, help, forgive.
- **Caring for others.** How can this care and concern for others and our world be lived out in a practical way? What suggestions do children have?
- **Belief.** Explain that the need for a strong personal belief and commitment and a wish to share it with others, is often an important concommitant for becoming a religious leader. What sort of things do the children have a certain belief and faith in? What sort of things do they believe are important?
- **Knowledge and training.** Many jobs require special knowledge and training. Think about some of these, e.g. teaching, nursing, the police. What sorts of things do you think a religious leader needs to know and be trained for?
- **Maths.** Collate and record on bar charts the different faith communities represented in school and the numbers of children belonging to them. Look at the shapes and symbols representing different religious groups.
- **History and geography.** On a local map, identify all religious buildings. Discover the dates when they were built. Which are most recent? Why? Visit as many as possible.

© 1993 Folens Ltd.

Religious Leaders in the Community

Here are three religious leaders in the community.

- Talk about which religions they belong to and write the answers underneath their pictures.
- Label any special features of their dress or the objects they are holding which identify them.

© 1993 Folens Ltd. This page may be photocopied for classroom use only

The Muslim Imam - Ideas Bank

Background

Related to the frames on the resource sheet.

1) Muslims worship in a mosque. The muezzin calls them to prayer from a minaret (tall tower). The mosque is considered a holy building - shoes are taken off. There are no pictures of Allah, or Muhammad. It is decorated with tiles or geometric patterns and lettering.
2) The imam has no priestly role. He is essentially the prayer leader - knowledgeable about the Qur'an. He wears a simple dress.
3) The imam has to ensure a constant supply of water so worshippers can wash before going into the prayer hall. Men and women rarely pray together in the mosque.
4) In the Zulla (prayer hall) Muslims always pray facing towards Mecca, their most holy city. The mirhab, a niche, indicates which direction to pray. Next to the mirhab there is often a minbar (a pulpit with steps) from which the imam gives his sermon on Friday (holy day).
5) In the mosque the imam and other teachers give daily lessons in Islam and Arabic to children.
6) One of the most pleasant duties of the imam is to observe the declaration of faith by those aspiring to become a Muslim - 'there is no God except Allah and Muhammad - peace be to him - is his servant and messenger'. Muslims believe that Muhammad was the last and true prophet of God (Allah), and through him God revealed his word as recorded in the Qur'an. Muslims also believe in Jesus, Moses and Abraham as prophets. All Muslims accept the same five duties as 'pillars of faith'. **a)** to confess their faith **b)** to pray five times a day **c)** to give alms to the needy **d)** to fast in Ramadan **e)** to make a pilgrimage to Mecca.
7) Ramadan - ninth month of the Muslim calendar - special because it was the month in which the prophet Muhammad first began to receive revelations from God. Muslims must fast for thirty days, each day from dawn to sunset. They must say extra prayers, try to read the whole of the Qur'an and to be particularly kind and helpful. The festival of Eid ul Fitr marks the end of Ramadan.
8) The imam will receive visits from any Muslims who require counselling. This is part of his pastoral role. There is no baptism for Muslim babies. Boys are circumcised soon after birth.
9) Marriages. The imam ensures the girl receives a gift from her husband; that the marriage is entered into freely; and solemnises the wedding. Muslim marriages are often arranged. They are joyous occasions for the whole community.
10) At funerals the imam officiates and prays. Before burial the body is washed and then wrapped in a shroud. No Muslim is ever cremated.
11) All imams have a community role. This may include visiting schools. In the evenings many mosques hold classes for Islamic education and act as community centres.
12) Increasingly, imams are taking part in ecumenical activities to discuss areas of common ground and interest with other religions.

Starting Points

- Ask an imam to come in and talk about his work. Muslim children can talk about their faith and the imam's role.
- Read and discuss the resource sheet together.
- Working in pairs, children randomly take one picture at a time, and tell each other what they can remember about each.

Activities

- **Write.** Children could use the pictures to help them write about the role of the imam or make up their own version of 'A Week in the Life of the Imam'.
- **Pillars of faith.** Why might they be called pillars? What do the children think of them? Copy them in their best writing and illustrate them.
- **Calligraphy.** Show the children some written Arabic. Explain that it is written from right to left. Copy some. Calligraphy was especially praised by Muslims as it was a way of reminding them of God's beautiful words in the Qur'an.

- **Ramadan and Eid.** Research and find out more about the reasons for these festivals and the customs connected with them.

© 1993 Folens Ltd.

The Muslim Imam

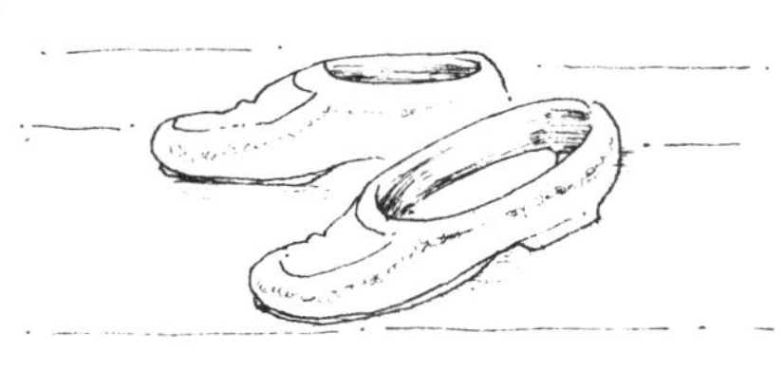

The mosque is holy. We take off our shoes when we enter.

I wear traditional dress in the mosque.

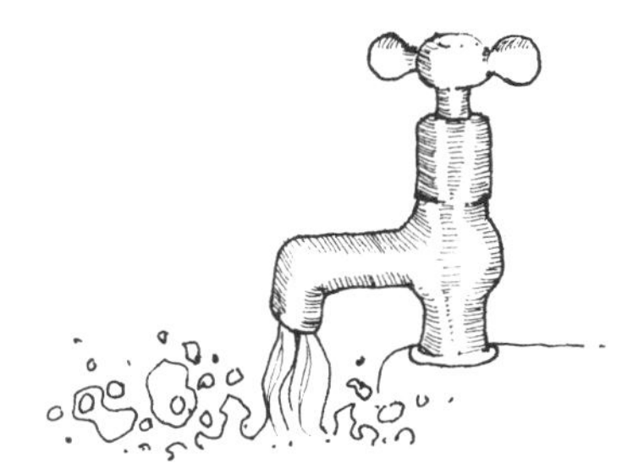

We have to wash before we pray.

It is important to pray regularly.

I teach children Arabic.

I love to hear people declare their faith.

At Eid, all Muslims put on their best clothes to pray at the mosque.

Sometimes I am invited to parties to celebrate a baby's birth.

A Muslim wedding is a very special occasion.

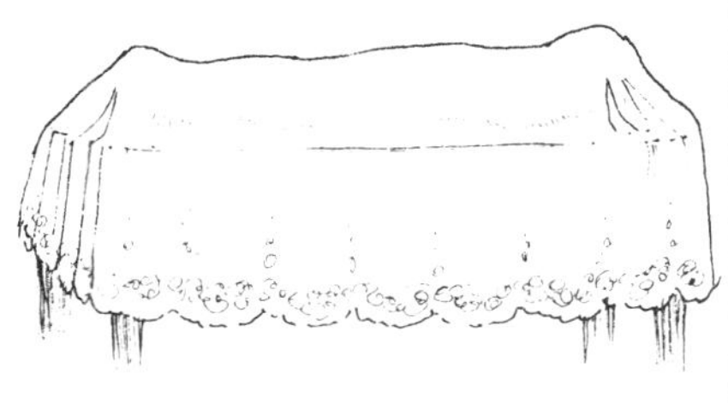

Funerals are sad times for all the family.

I often give talks in schools.

Sometimes I meet with other religious leaders in the community.

© 1993 Folens Ltd. This page may be photocopied for classroom use only

The Hindu Priest · Ideas Page

Background

Related to frames on the resource sheet.

1) The main religion in Indian sub-continent. Many Hindu communities in Britain. The Hindu priest often comes from within the community. The candidate may then be sent for a period of preparation and training in India.
2) Worship in a temple. Hindus worship many gods, although they all reflect different facets of the Lord of all creation, Brahma.
3) Hindus believe it is important to honour Brahma. Offering food is a symbolic act of reverence.
4) The main part of the priest's job is to lead the Hindu community in a religious capacity, in prayer (talking to God), worship (honouring God) and celebration (celebrating the goodness of God). There is no special day for worship like Sundays for the Christian. However, Hindus are encouraged to worship every day. There are nine 'special' days for worship each year. One of the most important Hindu festivals is Divali - a festival of light. It commemorates the triumph of Rama and Sita over the demon god - the triumph of good (light) over evil (darkness). Diva (clay) lamps are lit everywhere as a symbol of light.
5) Young Hindu children are blessed by the priest in the temple. This is often accompanied by a 'Thread Ceremony' for other brothers and sisters to symbolise the responsibilities the eldest has for the younger members of the family.
6) For religious ceremonies and rituals he wears special traditional clothes - loin cloth (a dhoti - ankle length), and a shirt with no collar (Jabbo).
7) Responsible for the temple. Ceremonially washes the statues as an act of reverence. Responsibility for preparing the temple for worship.
8) Hindus believe all life is sacred and should live out this principle which, in practical terms, means showing respect, gentleness and kindness to others. This respect extends to animals too. For example, the cow is considered sacred and many Hindus are vegetarians.
9) Much of the priest's work involves supporting other Hindus in the community. This frequently involves visiting homes. The priest encourages the community to work with love and to show love to others because Hindus believe their God is full of love and joy.
10) The priest regularly visits homes to perform religious rites. When a family moves into a new house, the priest will often visit and oversee the lighting of a fire as an offering to the fire god Agni, fire symbolising warmth, the cooking of meals, light and knowledge.
11) The priest officiates over key events in people's lives. Hindu weddings are especially joyful occasions.
12) Bereavement is followed by a quick cremation. After presiding, the priest will then visit the household immediately to conduct hymns and prayers and to comfort the family. Hindus believe in reincarnation or re-birth. Their reincarnated form is related to the sort of life they have led. The better their life the better position they believe they will be born into, and the closer they will get to God.

Starting Points

- Ask a Hindu priest to come in and talk about his work. Hindu children can talk about their faith and the priest's role.
- Read and discuss the resource sheet together.
- Working in pairs, children randomly take one picture at a time, and tell each other what they can remember about each.

Activities

- **Write.** Children could use the pictures to help them write an extended version of the responsibilities and roles of the Hindu priest, or alternatively use it as a basis for making up their own version of 'A Week in the Life of a Hindu Priest'.
- **Reincarnation.** What animal/class would children like to be born into in a future life? Discuss the sacred nature of life to Hindus and reasons for vegetarianism.
- **Festivals and celebrations.** Follow up the mention of Divali by finding out more about the story. Children could learn and sing a Divali song, learn more about festive food or make up mendhi designs for their hands (by finding out about the mendhi paste used by Hindus). Joss sticks could be lit and their different smells discussed. Consider how some festivals are connected with the seasons too, e.g. Holi, a Spring festival associated with Krishna, Divali an Autumn festival of lights.

© Folens Ltd.

The Hindu Priest

I am a Hindu Priest.

In our temple there are statues of many gods.

We have ceremonies offering food to Brahma, the Lord of Creation.

One of our biggest festivals, Divali, celebrates the triumph of good over evil.

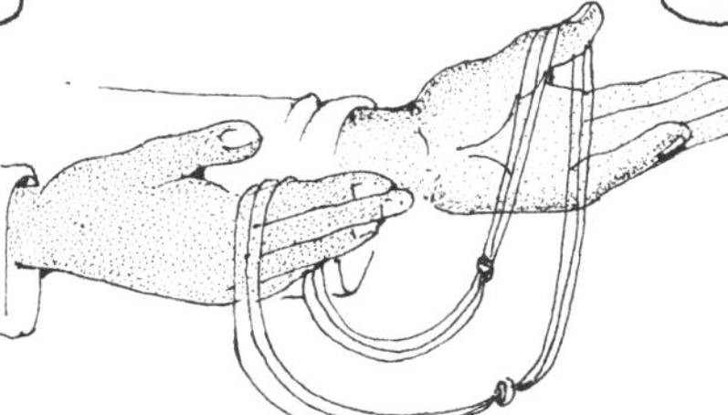

Another interesting ceremony I perform is called the 'Thread Ceremony'.

When I am working in the temple I wear traditional dress.

It is my responsibility to look after the temple.

We believe we should live our lives showing kindness to others.

I often visit people at home.

When people move into a new house I conduct a fire-lighting ceremony.

I enjoy marrying couples. It is such a happy occasion.

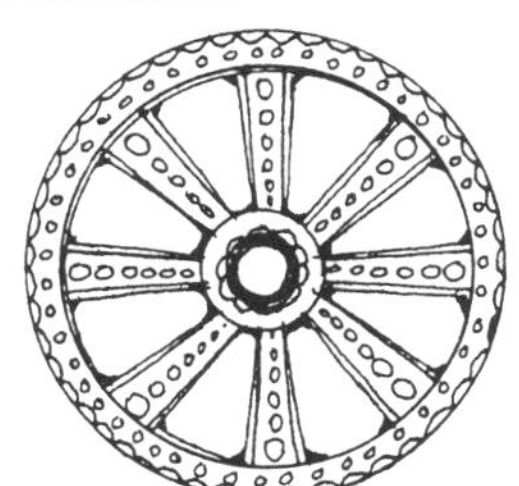

When people die, Hindus believe they are re-born as another person or animal.

© Folens Ltd. This page may be photocopied for classroom use only

The Christian Minister - Ideas Page

Background

Consider the roles of Christian ministers from other denominations using a similar framework if desired. Notes are related to frames on resource sheet.

1) Christian worship (offering praise to God) often takes place in a church on a Sunday.

2) The formality of the minister's dress (dog collar, cassock, surplice) accentuates the special priestly role of the minister. The crook he sometimes carries for ceremonial purposes symbolises that he is seen as a shepherd looking after his flock.

3) Infant baptism is important in the Church of England. The child's life is dedicated to God by the parents, and Godparents agree to be responsible for the spiritual development of the child. The minister dips his finger into the holy water and makes a sign of the cross on the infant's forehead. NB Some denominations, e.g. the Salvation Army and the Quakers, do not believe in baptism.

4) Confirmation provides adults with an opportunity to affirm their commitment to Christ. It is a public declaration of faith. The minister will prepare the individual to make sure that the commitment is fully understood.

5) The minister officiates at church weddings. The couple take their matrimonial vows before God and exchange rings as a symbol of the wholeness of their love for each other. This is a happy time for all the family.

6) Holy Communion is a more solemn service of thanksgiving to God. To Christians it is a reminder that Christ gave his life for humanity. The service involves receiving bread (representing Christ's body) and wine (representing His blood). The service derives from the account of the Last Supper in Luke's Gospel.

7) The minister may delegate responsibility for Sunday school activities. Many ministers see the need to show a keen interest in youth work with the emphasis on personal and social growth.

8) Christians believe that through Christ sins can be forgiven and when they die they have the promise of eternal life in heaven. Funeral services are held at the church where thanks are given for the deceased person's life.

9) Christmas is a joyful time of great celebration. It is a time when the birth of Christ is celebrated with carol services, midnight communion, etc.

10) Easter is a major Christian celebration when Christians remember Christ's crucifixion on a cross (Good Friday). The cross has become an important symbol for Christians as a result. The sadness of Christ's death is tempered by the joy of his resurrection on Easter Sunday. Christ's triumph over death presents Christians with the hope of new life.

11) Each church will have a group of members of the congregation elected to make important decisions about maintaining the church, finances, evangelising, organising various church activities, etc. The minister attends these meetings.

12) The minister has the spiritual responsibility for the congregation and the community. People must have confidence in him and feel able to turn to him for advice and to share their concerns and spiritual problems, etc. During the week his pastoral responsibilities may take up to fifty per cent of his time.

Starting Points

- Ask a Christian minister to come in and talk about his work. Christian children can talk about their faith and the minister's role.
- Read and discuss the resource sheet together.
- Working in pairs, children randomly take one picture at a time, and tell each other what they can remember about each.

Activities

- **Write.** Children could use the pictures to help them write an extended version of the responsibilities and roles - 'A Week In The Life Of An Anglican Minister'.
- **Christianity.** This literally means following Christ. Share together the children's knowledge about the life and teaching of Jesus.
- **Church buildings.** Map local churches. Sketch or model one. Research its history. Consider its features - pulpit, font, etc. Think about the functions the church performs.
- **Names.** How many names can children discover that are related to jobs connected with Christianity? e.g. archbishop, deacon, vicar, curate, server, etc.
- **The role of women.** In the past, women have not played key roles in formal church leadership. Discuss why this might be.

© 1993 Folens Ltd.

The Christian Minister

Church bells ring to welcome Christians to Sunday worship.

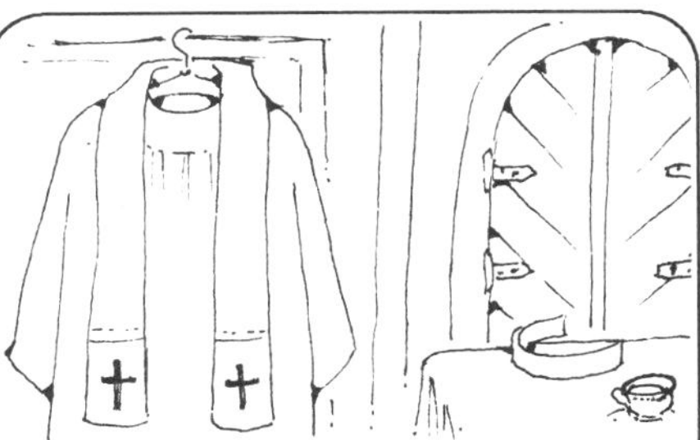
I wear special clothes to celebrate our church services.

The font is where I conduct baptism services.

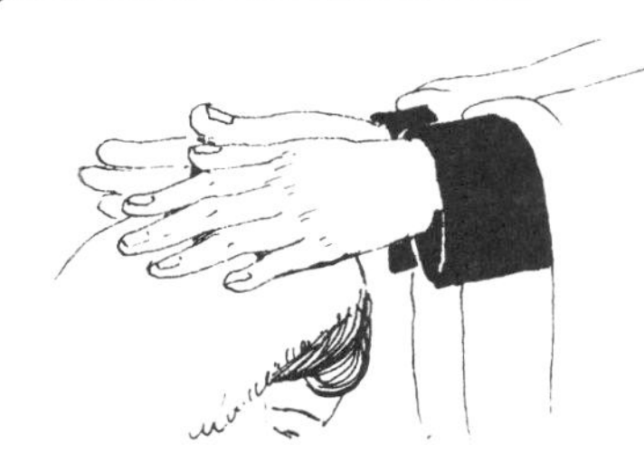
Confirmation is when adults confirm their commitment to Jesus Christ.

The marriage service is a very happy occasion.

At Holy Communion we remember that Christ died for us.

At Sunday school, children do lots of exciting activities.

Funerals can be sad, but Christians believe there is life after death.

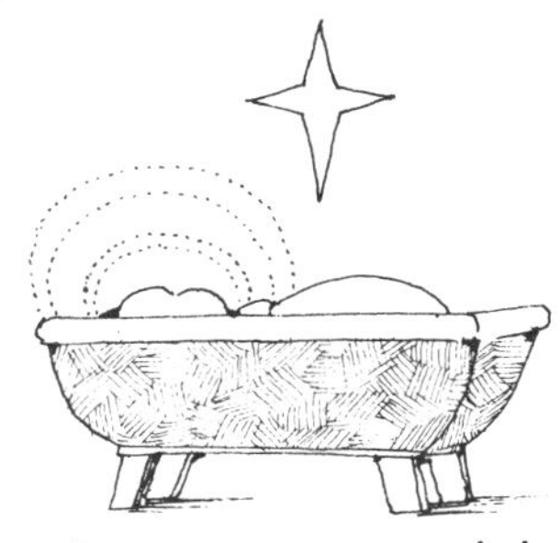
At Christmas we celebrate the birth of Christ.

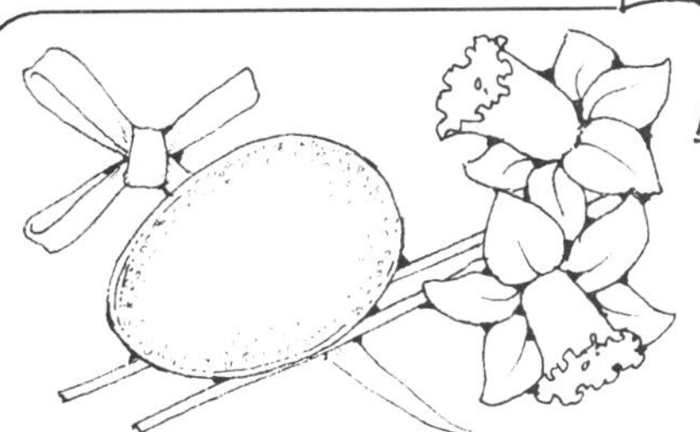
At Easter we remember when Jesus died but rose again. We celebrate his life.

I often have meetings with the church council.

During the week I visit many of my flock.

© 1993 Folens Ltd. This page may be photocopied for classroom use only

You can help - Ideas Page

Aim

The aim of this theme is to learn about the work of one group of people and one individual working together in a neighbourhood scheme providing help for the homeless. Children can appreciate some of their reasons for doing so and consider how this might be applied to their own individual situations.

Background

- Jeremy got involved in working in the community as a result of a school project, and began helping in a local soup kitchen. His interest and commitment long outlasted the demands of the school project.
- Jeremy worked with the homeless until he left home himself. He gave up hours and hours of his time in all weathers, whether he felt like it or not.
- He believed whole-heartedly in what he was doing and gained satisfaction out of doing the work. He did not do the work for public recognition and was surprised to find himself nominated for an award.
- He has seen the efforts of the group organising the work with the homeless go through struggles and successes. Jeremy has been delighted to be able to contribute to the growth of the Luton Day Centre.

Starting Points

- **Homelessness.** Look at the headlines on the resource sheet. Discuss what they are about. Get the children to explain the difference between a house and a home.
- What does being homeless mean? What might cause people to become homeless?
- Imagine what the problems of the long-term homeless might be. What would they do all day/all night? How would they survive? Where would they get food, money, shelter, medical care, etc?
- Are there homeless people in the neighbourhood? Who is responsible for the homeless?
- **The homeless around the world.** Collect pictures and news statistics to discuss the problems of the dispossessed and homeless throughout the world; the human misery of countless millions in large cities in the affluent countries and third-world countries; those made homeless through natural disasters like drought, flood, famine; those made homeless by human or avoidable disasters like civil war, etc.

Activities

- **CURA:** Look at the press cutting on the CURA soup kitchen (NB from the Latin word meaning caring). Discuss work of CURA. What sort of people are involved in running it (Christians, volunteers)? Matthew 25 v 31-40 is helpful in this respect. What might be the difficulties of setting up, resourcing and keeping such a project running?
- **The Luton Day Centre:** The Luton Day Centre evolved from the original soup kitchen idea. Read and discuss the sort of help and support it gives. Discuss especially the meaning of the words 'dignity and self-respect'.
- **Relief agencies.** Discuss the work of relief and aid agencies, and humanitarian organisations like Tear Fund, Cafod, Oxfam, etc.
- Read the articles on Jeremy Young. What can we learn from this about Jeremy? Why do you think he bothered to get involved?
- Discuss words like 'commitment', 'belief' and 'responsibility'.
- **Personal applications.** Sometimes the sheer scale and size of some of the problems we see around us is confusing. What can we as individuals do? Jeremy shows that it is possible to get involved and to make some sort of a contribution. Draw up some simple lists and discuss them.

Situations I need to think about.	Some people I need to think about.	Some ways I could think of others more.

- Do the children know of other people locally who are getting involved in helping others less fortunate than themselves?

You can help

Read the articles and decide why and how Jeremy Young helped people.

- *Write about the problems of the homeless:*
  What would they do all day and night? How would they survive?
  Where would they get money, food and shelter?
- *Use the headlines to write your own newspaper article.*

CURA's caring tasks

A SOUP kitchen for down-and-outs has been run in Luton for more than six years by an organisation known as CURA.

Run by a group of volunteers, CURA goes out three times a week to give soup, bread, warmth and often clothing to the homeless and needy of the town. On Monday lunchtime the venue is Beech Hill Methodist Church, Dunstable Road, and on Wednesday from 9 to 10 pm and Sunday from 5 to 6 pm the soup kitchen is run from the back hall of the Seventh Day Adventist Church in North Street.

Conceived in the minds of a small prayer group of Christians in Houghton Regis who wanted to help the homeless in the town, the organisation has grown and is now supported by all the major church denominations.

HOMELESS AND HUNGRY THEY COME

The Luton Day Centre for the Homeless opened its doors for the first time on December 27th 1989. It provides basic day-care for people sleeping rough, in squats and many who live alone in bedsits and cannot cope. Approximately 40-50 people come every day for help. The services in the Centre are run almost entirely by a magnificent team of volunteers.

Freshly cooked meals are served daily seven days a week. There is a nominal charge. In addition, from Mondays to Fridays people can get clean clothing, a hot shower, medical care, help and advice.

The dignity and self-respect of all people is important in all our activities and services.

Volunteer wins youth award

Jeremy Young, aged 17, of Stopsley Baptist Church, Luton, is one of 16 young people shortlisted from among hundreds to receive awards in this year's YMCA/BBC 'Today' Youth Awards (known until this year as 'The Best of British Youth Awards'), sponsored by the National Westminster Bank.

His voluntary work at the Luton Day Centre for the Homeless and running a non-alcoholic bar at his church greatly impressed the panel of judges, among whom were the BBC's 'Today' presenter, Brian Redhead.

Two years ago, Jeremy was required to do 15 hours, voluntary service as part of a school project and chose to help on a 'soup run' for homeless people. When its organisers extended the project to include a day centre based in eight converted flats, their young volunteer stayed to help. The Luton Day Centre for the Homeless offers meals, support, medical attention, advice and counsel to young people leaving care, runaways, 'down-and-outs' and alcoholics.

HOMELESS CENTRE GETS NEW HOME

SLOWLY FREEZING TO DEATH IN CARDBOARD CITY

ESCAPE ROUTE FROM DESPAIR

© Folens Ltd. This page may be photocopied for classroom use only

8 ways to help ...

There are many ideas in this book about developing and extending the photocopiable pages. Here are just eight ways to help you make the most of the **Ideas Bank** series.

1

Paste copies of the pages on to card and laminate them. The children could use water-based pens that can be wiped off, allowing the pages to be re-used.

2

Put the pages inside clear plastic wallets. They could be stored in binders for easy reference. The children's writing can again be easily wiped away.

3

If possible, save the pages for re-use. Develop a simple filing system so that the pages can be easily located for future use.

4

Use both sides of the paper. The children could write or draw on the back of the sheet, or you could photocopy another useful activity on the back.

5

Make the most of group work. Children working in small groups could use one page to discuss between them.

6

Photocopy the pages on to clear film to make overhead transparencies. The ideas can then be used time and time again.

7

Use the activity pages as ideas pages for yourself. Discuss issues and ideas with the class and ask the children to produce artwork and writing.

8

Customise the pages by adding your own activities. Supplement the ideas and apply them to your children's needs.

© 1993 Folens Ltd.